P9-DNN-450

VERY POSY

also by Posy Simmonds

MRS WEBER'S DIARY
TRUE LOVE
PICK OF POSY

Posy Simmonds

VERY POSY

JONATHAN CAPE
THIRTY-TWO BEDFORD SQUARE LONDON

To my mother

First published 1985
Reprinted 1986

Jonathan Cape Ltd, 32 Bedford Square, London WC1B 3EL

British Library Cataloguing in Publication Data

Simmonds, Posy
Very Posy.
I. Title
741.5'942 PN6737.S5

ISBN 0 224 02818 9

The drawings in this book have been taken from episodes of *The Silent Three*, a weekly cartoon strip appearing in the *Guardian*, and from *Harper's Magazine*, New York.

Printed in Great Britain by
St Edmundsbury Press, Bury St Edmunds, Suffolk

December 22

December 23

December 24

December 25

December 26

December 27

What's in Store

It was
And Jesus' birfday was a long, long time ago, wasn't it?

And why do we buy pwesents?
'Cos it's a very nice thing to do.

And it cheers us up in the dark winter... and we make everything look all pretty.. with the TREE, eh? And the holly...

And BALLOONS?
And CWACKERS?
Yes, all that, Benji...

We make it all lovely... and we have a nice time... and *Sometimes* there's SNOW.. but not usually....
And WOBINS?
OFTEN robins!

Right! Here we are!

Now.. hold my hand very TIGHT, Benji
No, this way, Benji! Up the escalator!
No, we're NOT going back to TOYS Benji!
French
Perfumes
Oh God!
..an' will dere be all lovely snow and reindeer? Will dere?
Ah... Shuddup Benji, will you!!

Music! Love! Laughter!
Something for ALL the FAMILY!
MOTHER GOOSE IN BLUNDERLAND
TV's Annie Foyse
with
Benny Vincent
&
"Barfie"
The Romolettes
The Sexational Hi-Kix!
Don Harp
Regal Palace THEATRE

The Weber family have just seen the *happiest, all-star family show* in town!
There! Now *wasn't* that **FUN**!
Now, what do we say to Daddy for taking us, eh? ... Manda?... Tamsin?
Where are those nice, **big THANK YOUS** ?
Here, I'll carry him.

What *ungrateful* children!
It was ***boring!***
Too ***long!***
Too much ***singing!***

Oh dear! Well, I thought it was all rather ***tuneful***...

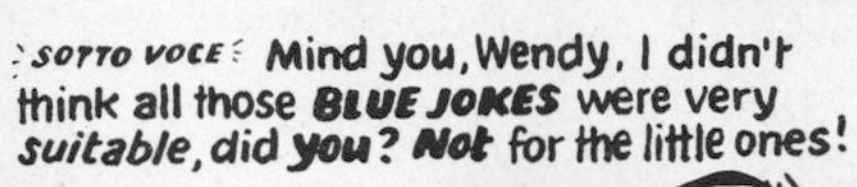

SOTTO VOCE: Mind you, Wendy, I didn't think all those **BLUE JOKES** were very *suitable*, did **you? Not** for the little ones!
Oh, I didn't mind **them** so much....
I thought they were ***absolutely REVOLTING!***

But some of those *little* girls were very clever, didn't you think?
What, the girls from the *Stage School*?
..Yes..rather artistic, I thought.

Oh I thought they were ***NAUSEATING!!***

All those **13** year olds in **G strings** & ***push-up*** bras full of cotton wool, ***stroking*** their hips & bleating "***Big Spender***"...
I nearly **VOMITED!**

Oh I thought **THEY** were rather ***funny***

Benny Vincent was quite good...
Oh, how **CAN** you, Wendy!
He was ***APPALLING!***

...mouthing off that ***telly-media-jaffa-cake-culture*** into the mike....
You only knew when to laugh when he gave that smirk of his....

Hilarious Family Fun!
MOTHER GOOSE IN BLUNDERLAND
TV's Annie Foyse
with
Benny Vincent
&
Barfie
The Romolettes
The Sexational Hi-Kix
Don Harp
"Something in it to **OFFEND ALL** the ***family!***" *Eh?*

Ooh dear, Jo.... they will take care, won't they?

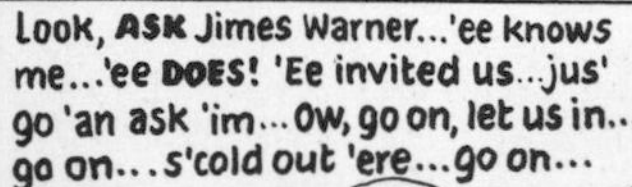

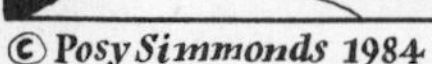

It is the Annual Dinner Dance of International Brewhouse Inc. *Edmund Heep* is on his own, (*Mrs Heep doesn't care for these occasions.*)...and as the evening draws to a close, Edmund finds himself in *purdah*....

...*no one* will dance with him....

...he is subjected to disapproving looks...

This is *odd*. A combination of distinctive wines and delicious eats *should* have made the company well disposed to *all* its fellows.

International Brewhouse Inc

ANNUAL DINNER
Monday 21st December 1981

PROGRAMME
Grace
Loyal Toast
Presentation to M.J. Wilkes
Dancing to Spooks Disco
Tombola
Raffle Draw

Menu
Grapefruit or Tuna Cocktail
Suprême de Volaille Havana
Garden Peas
Buttered Sweet Corn
Croquette Potatoes
Rum Baba / Coupe Cardinal
Le Fromage
Devilled Roe Savoury
Coffee & Mints

Edmund is puzzled by their chilly manner...

...especially as, *before* dinner, he has been a *Good Samaritan*...

And so, during the coffee and mints...

....Edmund rises to the occasion:

Timor Mortis
A contagious virus has wiped out Keith, the remaining Weber guinea pig....
Right, now we put him in...
Glawy be to the Father and to the Son and into the hole he goes
Ghost!
Ssjoopid!
A few hours prior to this sad scene......
How are the children taking it, Wendy?
Oh, they didn't seem bothered at ALL when I told them...
..just asked me what would happen to Keith next......
Yes, they asked ME that... what did you say?
And me.
Well, I told them the TRUTH... I said we'd bury Keith in one of Manda's old Lego boxes in the garden...and that, after a bit, he'd become a little skeleton....
Oh, Wendy! NO!
How could you!
Well, they're horrid, unsentimental little SO&SOS...they've shown NO concern at all... not even when Keith was ill!
Anyway, I've had ENOUGH! That's the last lot I'm having...WHO is it that's had to look after the animals all the time? MUGGINS, that's who!
Same MUGGINS who gets landed with the school gerbils every holidays.... It's ME who spent all Christmas worried stiff that the whole bloody lot would CROAK in the cold weather!
Wendy! REALLY!
Well, what did YOU tell them?
Well...I mentioned GOD...& said Keith's little spirit had gone to Heaven.
Oh..
Ah...
George...what did you say?
I said: Keith's BODY had died, but he lived on in our MINDS, because we remembered him and missed his squeaks....
Keith
Hallo Keith!
KEITH
We liked Granny's idea best

Wendy Weber likes to keep part of the day to *herself*.... ..a *private* time, when she can loose the reins of *domesticity* and continue working on her thesis......

...or, sometimes, if the Muse fails:

Oh **Momma**! I don't **care**! I'm gonna **keep** this **BABY**...and I'm gonna do it **RIGHT**! I'm gonna be a **real** mother!

GASP Why, Donna!

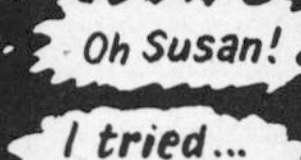

You **NEVER** let me **ALONE**! You couldn't **CUT** the **CORD**! SOB You **fussed**! You **stuffed** me full of home made **cookies**!

Dining with one's husband's colleagues is one of the favours an academic's wife feels bound to bestow.....

....but this is a *bit* MUCH: having to help butter up a visiting member of the Board of External Assessors, on whose *fateful* report the standing of the faculty depends.....

A RIDDLE:

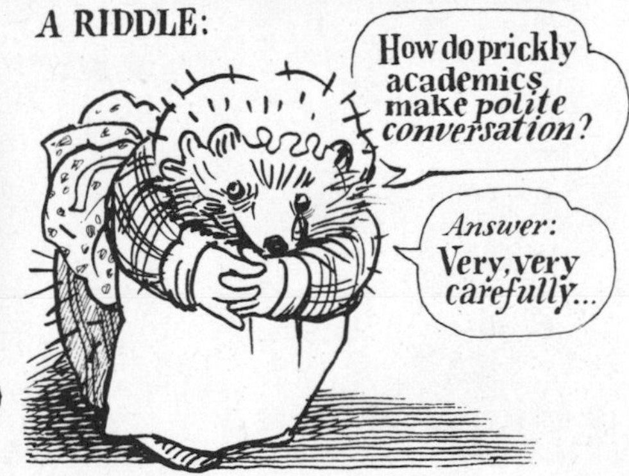

Full Stretch
At this stage of the academic year, Senior Lecturers are often tense & burdened with care....particularly those to whom the Dean has just re-introduced the idea of Early Retirement....
FEMMES
SOLLERS
Here is George Weber calming his troubled mind, with his 35 minute yoga programme....
The Half Lotus
True...I'm bloody sick of the Poly... been there far too long...
..Next year'll be my twentieth intake of new students...
Ooof!
The Plough
..All those new faces... totally knackering...
..and what with the cuts..I've got far more lectures...Far bigger tutorial groups...more and more pressure....
Oof!
The Stretched Triangle
..more & more MEETINGS...
..bloody Space Allocation Committee...
.. the new extension planning...God! I've had it up to here!
The Cat
..and my only friend on the Governing Body's resigning....
Sitting Rotation
...Robbe-Grillet's become passé..
..and I just can't keep up with Women's studies....
The Cobra
..and my lectures!...God! I've given "Hegemony of the Mark"...and "Planned Cultural Obsolescence" TEN years running!!!
Be able to double-glaze the bedroom
...see the kids more...
No more Sunday night lecture preparation...
Be good for me to retire... stretch myself a bit...
Wendy'd be free to work full time...
..could do my book...
..really get into de Man
..I could... ..I could...
The Tree
..but that great lump of salary every month... ...I couldn't really... could I...?
The Chicken
© Posy Simmonds 1983

Shifting Values
George Weber's aunt has left him a painting.... one which she considers valuable.....
Don't like it...
Something very MEAN about the paint...
mm..it's altogether rather mean...
...rather a nasty little daub...
Who is?

Still, maybe we ought to let an EXPERT look at it before we give it to the jumble...

And so...to a London gallery:
26 GILPIN fine art

We-ll..oh, I think we've got something FRIGHTFULLY interesting here....
..could be wrong...

It's signed 'PWS' rind abite 1887 ...I think it could be an early Wilson Steer...it's tremendously suggestive of him.....
!
!

I MAY be sticking my neck ite... but he DID a lot of landskip... beaches, like this...
..lots of surface glitter...dazzly sands ...lovely, limpid backgrinds....
Period's ABSOLUTELY right...
It's very, very pretty!

But could you BEAR it if I shewed it to my colleague? It's so very much his 'scene'...English Neo-Impressionism...
Of course

Charles.. have you got a sec?
I can see rather more in it now it's put in context, Wendy...
Amazing! A Steer!
It grows on you
It is rather pretty, you know...
God! So it must be worth......

That? Oh, that's our STEER.. pretty, isn't it?

Oh dear... I'm afraid it doesn't seem to be a Steer...

But it is TREMENDOUS fun!
Yes, isn't it!
It's not quite right... such a shame, I LOVE those little naif figures.. ...very sweet....

I think it's by a lesser artist than Steer.... & certainly by someone SMITTEN with George Clausen...

I suppose if one wanted to be a CARPING CRITIC, one might say that the colour is somewhat over-saturated.... Something a weeny bit WONKY about the composition..
Yes, I wondered abite that...

But it is such a very JOLLY little painting... TERRIFIC fun!...must give you a lot of pleasure!
Yes, well thank you

Yes, well we thought it was rather a mean sort of painting, didn't we?
I had my dites abite it, all along!

D.I.Y.
When it's time for the ritual appeasement of the Lares & Penates.. (the household gods)....
IT'S A BLOODY TIP, THIS HOUSE!
THEY NEVER DO ANYTHING TO IT!!
IT'S UNBEARABLE!
...Mere mortals are only aware of a malaise.... which occurs, particularly in the Spring, or on returning from summer holiday... when they see their home with fresh eyes.... and groan...
It's a bloody TIP, this house!
We never do ANYTHING to it!!!
It's Unbearable!
And it is unbearable... with its filthy cork tiles, peeling up at the corners...
THE CEILINGS KIPPERED WITH NICOTINE!
OLD HESSIAN WALL-PAPER COMING UNSTUCK AT THE SEAMS!
AND YOU SHOULD SEE THE STATE OF THE DOWNSTAIRS LAVATORIUM!!
The GODS must be appeased, and a ritual object must be chosen for sacrifice:
What if we stripped all the old paint off the sitting-room door?
That'd be a start..
AND NOW THE APPEASEMENT BEGINS:
THE MORTALS BREAK MILK BOTTLES. THE GLASS IS USED TO CHIP OFF THE OLD PAINT:
Bloody stupid idea, this GLASS! OW!
John said it worked!
THEN THEY GO OUT AND BUY SCRAPERS & PAINT STRIPPER.. & ANOINT THE DOOR:
Doesn't go very far, this stripper
Why d'you have to put it in the egg saucepan?
THEN THEY BUY MORE PAINT STRIPPER:
SPEEDI STRIPP
THEN THEY BUY 2 PAIRS OF RUBBER GLOVES....
Ooh, my hands! Bloody burns this stuff!
...AND GO OUT AGAIN TO BUY A SPECIAL SORT OF SCRAPER TO DO THE MOULDINGS ROUND THE PANELS:
God, we've ruined the mouldings!
Tsk!
THEY RUN OUT OF STRIPPER AGAIN & ONLY 1/3 OF THE DOOR IS DONE. BUT ONE OF THE MORTALS HAS HEARD OF GAS PAINT STRIPPERS....
AND GOES OUT & BUYS ONE...
Ooh! This is better!
..AND SCORCHES THE DOOR.
Oh Sh**!!
..AND HAS TO BUY SAND-PAPER..AND WHEN THIS IS TO NO AVAIL, GOES OUT AGAIN AND BUYS A PERMANENT ABRASIVE DISC FOR HIS DRILL...
..AND MAKES CIRCULAR GOUGE MARKS AGAINST THE GRAIN...
Oh God! George!
!
...AND SWEARS PITEOUSLY....
****!
..AND HIS SPOUSE SUGGESTS THAT AS THE SURFACE IS RUINED, WHY DON'T THEY PANEL IT WITH HARDBOARD, BOTH SIDES... THEN, IT'LL LOOK LIKE A MODERN, FLUSH DOOR...
..SO THEY GO & BUY 2 SHEETS OF 8' x 4' HARDBOARD, AND PUT IT ON THE ROOF RACK... AND CUT IT TO SIZE.. AND THERE'S A LOT OF WASTE, AS THE DOOR IS 6'6" x 3'6"..
EHEU!
...THEY TEMPER IT...AND LEAVE IT TO DRY OVERNIGHT...AND THE NEXT DAY, THEY HAMMER IT ON BOTH SIDES OF THE DOOR...AND IT LOOKS ABSOLUTELY TERRIFIC....
...EXCEPT...NOW THE DOOR IS THICKER THAN THE ARCHITRAVE...
And the **?!*!!! door won't SHUT!
..AND THE MORTALS SCREAM:
SOD this for a laugh Why don't we just BUY a new door!!
And the household gods are appeased... ...and the mortals pour themselves large libations....
GETTING A NEW DOOR, ARE WE?
TRIFFIC, INNIT?

Act 1 takes place in a richly appointed home, where *Trish*, a wife & mother, is swearing piteously at the tumble drier, which has again betrayed her...

She bemoans her lot as Drudge ...& a husband who considers her tasks trivial.

Oh: ****! ♪

Enter *Stanhope*, her spouse, a middle-aged burgher. He berates her: what has *she* to bewail? Does *he* not toil a 30 hour week, whilst she has:-

Heartsick, *Trish* tells him just *where* he can shove the rest of the week's washing.
Stanhope departs, singing a gay *arioso*....

Chorus:
♪ Yes! He'll just go and shove it in the Launderette! ♪ ♪

Act 2 opens in a sombre *Launderama*. Unknown to *Stanhope*, the overseer is an *OGRESS*. Fearing her *terrible* ire, washer-persons cower behind their newspapers. A mood of foreboding is struck in a tense, nervous *aria*, sung by a flat-dweller, *"Oh Sheets I wouldst have folded!"*

As *Stanhope* enters, the *Ogress* rises.....

Boldly, *Stanhope* declines. He tries to open a washing machine.... It does not yield. He forces it. He overloads it. He over-soaps it...chooses too hot a programme...slams the door...rams the *wrong* money in...

An orchestral interlude follows, representing a *tempest*. A grim washer-folk chorus prays to the gods...

Help, oh help this stupid burgher!

In a brilliant *coloratura aria*, the *Ogress* rebukes *Stanhope*....

There follows a duet, where *Stanhope* apologises & the *Ogress*, *touched to the core*, *reveals* her true identity: a tender-hearted woman, turned to steel by the demands of her job.

At her words, the scales fall from *Stanhope's* eyes: he begins to appreciate the long hours & pongs which most women have to endure...including his wife.

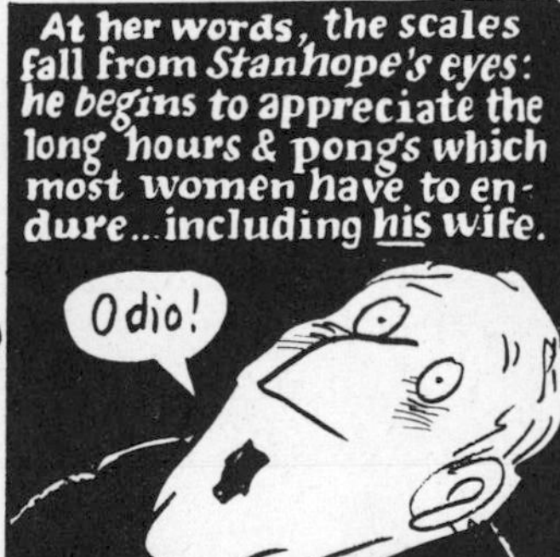

The final Act finds *Stanhope* reunited with *Trish*. He pledges a life of *shared* lather...

Custom and *Infidelities* have damped down the fire in *Stanhope* and *Trish's* marriage....

But occasionally, the odd *ember* glows:

Acting one's age
TRE BAR
In a crowded theatre bar, during the interval, Stanhope Wright spots some talent....
THINKS
I could make a great PLAY for you.....
For two nights only
MAJESTIC
Stanhope Wright in "I, ROGER..."
First Act
Second Act
Interval
Third Act
Applause
Curtains
THINKS
I could make a great PLAY for you...
"I LAUGHED! I CRIED! SHEER HEAVEN!
"THIS SHOULD RUN & RUN & RUN!"
"FELICITY DRAPKIN A JOY AS THE MISTRESS!
"STANHOPE WRIGHT-BEST LOVER EVER!"
TWICE DAILY!
STANHOPE WRIGHT
FELICITY DRAPKIN
IN
...THE MICE WILL PLAY!
Now in its 4th West End year!
"A SEXY SOUFFLÉ".
"IF EVERY NIGHT OUT COULD BE LIKE THIS!"
"THE GREAT REJUVENATOR!
Stanhope's cool collapses when his love-life sours yet again! 6.10 pm.
6.0 News
with Anthea Dobbs
Weatherman
6.10 It Always Ends in Tears
(Repeat) 43rd episode
Daft sit-com, featuring yet another disastrous liaison for jaded ad-man, Stanhope Wright, in his ill-fated bid to cope with the male menopause.
Produced by Keith Handyside
Series editor Gary Rothschild
© Posy Simmonds 1982

..And no Questions asked....
It is the morning after the night before.....

Thinks:
Him: ?
Her: Where am I?

Hallo!..
Good morning...
Him: Who are you?
!

Well...fancy..!
Yes..!
Oh God! I didn't did I? Oh God!
God! We did! Didn't we?

I'll make some coffee...
Lovely...
God! Was I drunk? Oh God in heaven!
Aren't we going to make love?

Sleep well?
Wonderfully!
Why did I do it?!
It's all been a mistake, hasn't it?

Can I use some of your cleansing cream?
Help yourself!
It's your wife's, isn't it?
Only, put it back where you found it, for God's sake..!

Nice house you've got.
Yes.. I like it...
How long's your wife away for?
How am I going to get rid of you?

Sorry about the wine on your carpet....
Oooh.... Don't worry...
Will your wife smell a rat?
How the HELL am I going to explain that?

Quite big... your house...
Big enough...
Those your kids?
Godsake, stop NOSING!

Ah well.. DUTY calls, worse luck...
Yes..it does!
You want me to p*ss off, don't you?
Aren't you ever going to get dressed?

Thanks to you...I feel really great this morning!
Ah...
Oh God, Trish'll find out about this...she always does!
Aha!

Look...I want you to know that what happened last night...I...er...don't make a habit of it....
No no!
I do try to be discreet
B*lls... you do it all the time, don't you?

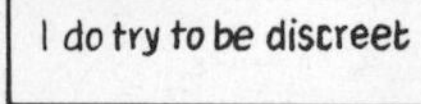

So: Well, this has been very special..... thank you...
Yes, it has...
SNIFF

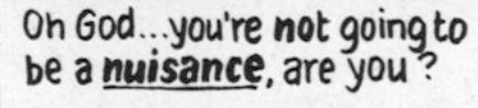

Oh God...you're not going to be a nuisance, are you?
I shan't see you again, shall I?

...Our.. SPECIAL secret...
SNIFF

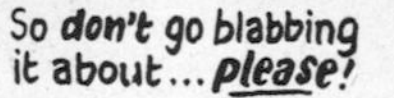

So don't go blabbing it about... please?
You SWINE!

See you around... Ciao!
See you
Phew!
Huh!

But just one question..
Just one question...

WHY did you do it if it makes you feel so MISERABLE?
Why did you do it if it makes you feel so GUILTY?

MEN
at
Work

Morning has broken at International Brewhouse Inc.
You're bright and early, Edmund!
Oh, hallo, Bull's wool!

Stone me! Valentines! Who they for?
That little Pam ... & little Linda in Accounts... you know, the one with the big boots...

KENT & SONS
Darling!
be Mine
Here... you don't think these'll offend, do you?

Ah! They're lovely girls... both of 'em....
POSTIE, POSTIE, DO YOUR DUTY — TAKE THIS TO MY HOT PATOOTIE!
S.W.A.L.K.
I LOVE YOU A LOT, I LOVE YOU ALMIGHTY I WISH MY PYJAMAS WERE NEXT TO YOUR NIGHTIE!!!
LOVE FROM YOUR CONSTANT BEDMATE
Tony Chestnut
Who's this Tony Chestnut, Edmund?

Tony Chestnut? You know him! You sleep with him too! Haa!
What!?

You sleep with Toe...
..Knee...

..Chest..
...Nut!
Haahaa!

Oh God!
WaHa HARha HAR HAR haaa!!

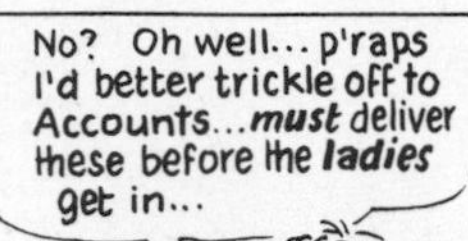
No? Oh well... p'raps I'd better trickle off to Accounts... must deliver these before the ladies get in...

Here's little Linda..

'STRUTH!
Linda

God in heaven!
Gordon Bennet!

Ooh dear!

Horrible they were...
Tell us, Edmund!
All chest mats & enormous winkles!
Winkles! Blimey!

They only put 'em up to provoke..
Makes you feel inadequate doesn't it?
Well, it's degrading... bloody offensive
The dirty little MARES!
They're only pictures, Edmund... REAL men aren't like that!
Linda

Liaison

* LOCAL EDUCATION AUTHORITY

* NATIONAL ASSOCIATION OF TEACHERS IN FURTHER & HIGHER EDUCATION

Not with that bunch of computer-merchants!

Hardly user-friendly, are they?

You can't mean.... AMALGAMATE the two departments?!

er.. Yes

Not with that bunch of artsy-fartsy LEFTIES!

* HER MAJESTY'S INSPECTOR

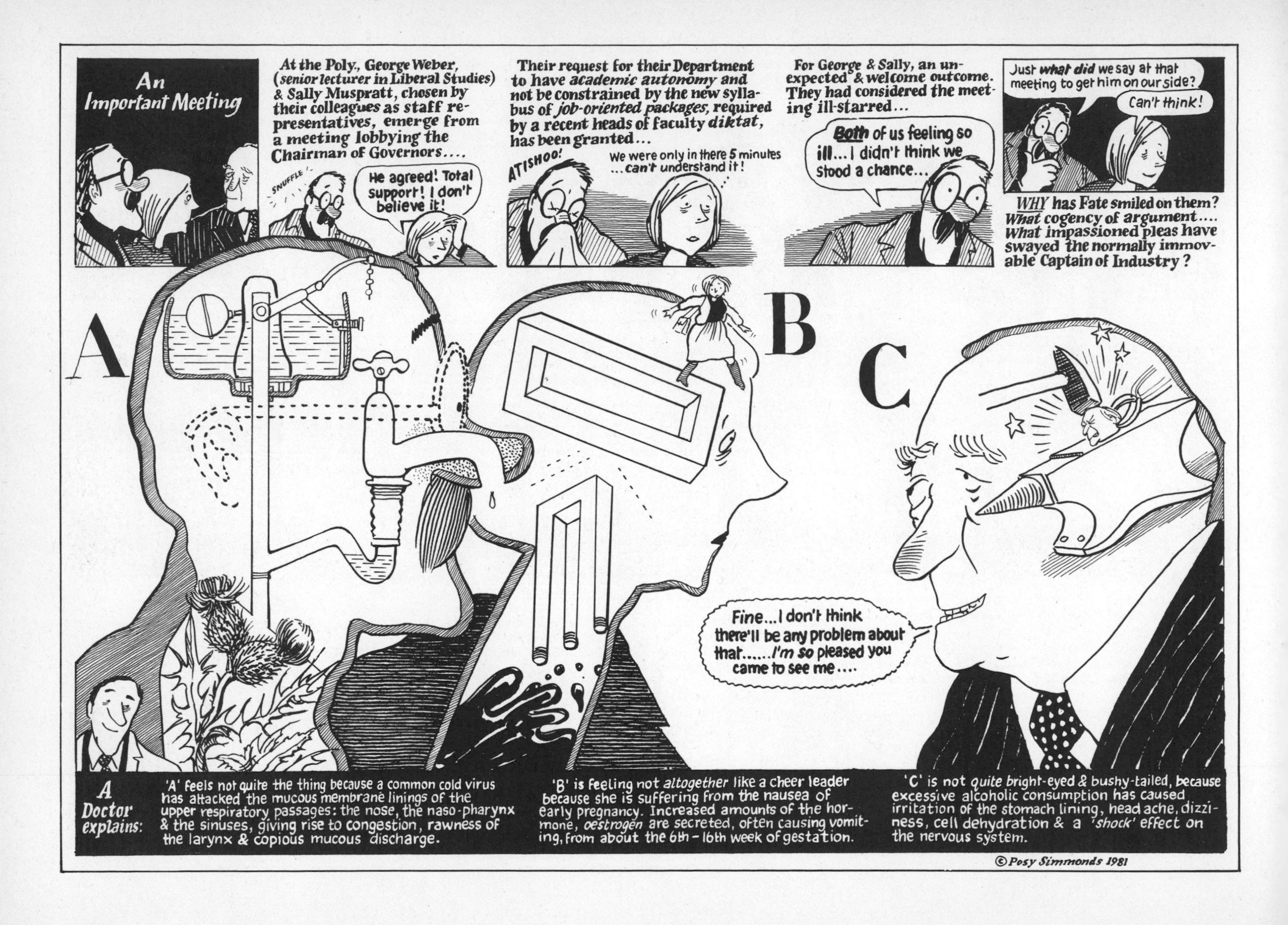
An Important Meeting
At the Poly., George Weber, (senior lecturer in Liberal Studies) & Sally Muspratt, chosen by their colleagues as staff representatives, emerge from a meeting lobbying the Chairman of Governors....
SNUFFLE!
He agreed! Total support! I don't believe it!
Their request for their Department to have academic autonomy and not be constrained by the new syllabus of job-oriented packages, required by a recent heads of faculty diktat, has been granted...
ATISHOO!
We were only in there 5 minutes ...can't understand it!
For George & Sally, an unexpected & welcome outcome. They had considered the meeting ill-starred...
Both of us feeling so ill... I didn't think we stood a chance...
Just what did we say at that meeting to get him on our side?
Can't think!
WHY has Fate smiled on them? What cogency of argument.... What impassioned pleas have swayed the normally immovable Captain of Industry?
A
B
C
Fine... I don't think there'll be any problem about that......I'm so pleased you came to see me....
A Doctor explains:
'A' feels not quite the thing because a common cold virus has attacked the mucous membrane linings of the upper respiratory passages: the nose, the naso-pharynx & the sinuses, giving rise to congestion, rawness of the larynx & copious mucous discharge.
'B' is feeling not altogether like a cheer leader because she is suffering from the nausea of early pregnancy. Increased amounts of the hormone, oestrogen are secreted, often causing vomiting, from about the 6th - 16th week of gestation.
'C' is not quite bright-eyed & bushy-tailed, because excessive alcoholic consumption has caused irritation of the stomach lining, head ache, dizziness, cell dehydration & a 'shock' effect on the nervous system.
©Posy Simmonds 1981

Black Looks
On his return from making a special bargain-offer wine purchase, George Weber looks pale and wan:
What's the matter, George?
What is it?
MARQUES DE BONBAROLO
LOGROÑO
Rioja

I've just had a repetition of a HORRIBLE experience!
What? What's happened?
Rioja
Rioja

They all STARED at me! They stared at me..... with that SAME look...
Who did?!

...that SAME huddle of black overcoats! ...SAME as twenty five years ago!
Who?
I can't BEAR it!
What overcoats?
What look?

Oh, it's a terrible look, Wendy... ..black huddle of clothes... Look of ENVY... blunt ENVY...and DERISION! Oh heck! Utter DERISION!
You mean like those peasants looked at us in Crete?
K. ΣΥΡΙΩΤΑ
Oh Kalimera

No! Far worse!
...25 years ago, I got that look...when I was down from Oxford in the vac...my FATHER & his mates all STARED...
Rioja

Oh God! That look! It said: "All right for some, you jammy b*gg*r!"
STOUT
ALES
THE K

You mean, they're outside here now! Your father and his friends?
No no no!

Well, WHO're you talking about, for God's sake!? WHO's just stared at you?
Just now... outside the house ...Belinda & her jobless friends...

I see...so there you were, unloading all the Rioja out of the Volvo....
Yes...and they stared at me!

Rioja
TEACHER'S

Yeah! The way your Dad looked at us, Belinda... Well pleased with himself!

Nature, Nurture (& Nutrition)

Belinda Weber has eschewed Further Education, in favour of a little job, helping cook for a Directors' Dining Room:

We did this really brilliant thing for them, today, Mum... Coronation Chicken... ..you get chicken breasts, right?......

...you whiz up curry powder in mayonnaise... slosh it on ...real doddle, I tell you...
RAW curry powder?
Bottle mayonnaise?
Yeh
God's truth!

..then we did this choccy Roulade...
..and TOMORROW, we're doing this cheese cake...one of the drectors goes really BARMY over it!
That's Alisdaire..the one with the SAAB..he's really nice...he asked me for my phone number...
ANYWAY..you get all cream cheese,'n'cream,'n' a tin of mandarins 'n' all these ginger biccies...
Sounds QUITE disgusting!

'Snot! They really love it!
And they KNOW about food!
Really?

Well, they wouldn't touch YOUR sort of lentil-peasant crap!
They like a bit of class!

Look...run away, Belinda, would you? I've got this essay to do...the supper to get and the twins from Brownies...

Why you so FOUL to me?! Why you SO bloody about my job?!

Because it's a silly, filling-in-time-till-marriage job! You and your 'A' Levels...you ought to be at UNIVERSITY...or training for a proper career!

But I don't WANT a CAREER!!
!

I wanna marry someone RICH! A rich company director!
I wanna SAAB!

I wanna have a nice HOUSE! I don't wanna live in a conversion in an up & coming neighbourhood!!

I never want a pine dresser or roller blinds...or ANYthing PATCHWORK!!

I NEVER, EVER want to eat another lentil... kidney bean! I'm SICK of brown rice!! I wanna eat Cordon Bleu! I wanna have proper dinner parties!

Oh well...if that's the way you feel....
Yeah! I DO!

And I'm sorry... I can't help it...
..it was the way I was brought up...

Here are the Webers and friends *à table*....

A Senior Lecturer *explains*:

Erm...

..& cassoulet DOES freeze so wonderfully...

..and it's what Aunt Gwen would have wanted us to do... so...

One is not disposed to subject the anxious interplay of TABOO & the AESTHETICS of NOURISHMENT to mechanical analysis... erm...

To do so would be to impoverish a theme rich in oppositions: *Vegetable/Animal*...*Live/Dead*...*Heaven/Earth*... ..*Hot/Stone Cold*...

We can see the *cassoulet* as a mediator, *inter-generationally* ...the link in the chain...er... *Goethe's unendliche Kette*...

Oh, Dad! Please! Why not?
Why can't we stop somewhere & eat?
You NEVER treat us... you're SO mean!!!
Please Please Dad!
YOU'RE always eating out, Dad!
We only want fish'n'chips!
My tummy HURTS!
I'll only be sick again if I don't eat!
WHY can't we?
You're so bloody selfish, Dad!
You never take us ANYWHERE!
Please Dad!
We've got to stop and wee anyway!
Midway through a horrible journey of car-sickness, bickering and unreasonable demands.....
No we can't!
Because I say so!
Because it's too expensive!
Because the food's usually such godawful MUCK in England...
God knows, we get the food we de-serve, over here..
But I don't want you lot to get used to eating it....
...Your generation must be the one that com-plains about it...
No one ever bloody complains!
No, Tamsin we are NOT stopping!
Nevertheless, the Weber family find themselves à table in the genial atmosphere of a Pally Inn....availing themselves of that Special Wayfayrers' Welcome With a Difference.....
Cheer up Dad
Wayfayrers' Welcome
at PALLY INNS
Soon they are tucking into petite, fibrous mats of steak, viridian peas, flaccid chips, served in a flourish of wicker and paper...great salvers of industrial salad creme...suit cases of pastry, filled with sickly, apple gum.......
Rather cute!
And have you had a lovely dinner?
Well, isn't your Daddy kind!
Aren't you a lucky girl then!
Everything all right for you, was it, sir?
Oh ve-ry nice!
Lovely thank you
Nice to see a family out altogether...
All enjoying themselves, bless their hearts!
What a lovely family!
And everything all right for you, sir?
PRAYER: We've paid the bill...let's just go! Don't, George! Don't say it! I can't take it today...just don't, don't, Don't!
And all you young ladies ...& the young man...had a nice meal, have we!?
!
Yes! Lovely!
Yass!
Yes!
Look..no, we haven't, actually... ...sorry to say this...but it was FILTHY! Tasteless!...... Heavings! FOUL!
Crap!
YUK!
Horrible behaviour!
Well, you feel so sorry for the child-ren, don't you...
Well, ours was delicious, wasn't it Beryl?
Tsk! really!
I'm afraid his steak was a teeny bit overdone...
Well, really!
SO RUDE!
No manners!
D'you think they're those left wing sort of types?
very uncalled for...
Tsk!

It's lonely in Tresoddit when the fleet's away...

The little hamlet holds its breath and gazes out to sea and waits for the safe return of its wayfaring ones.....

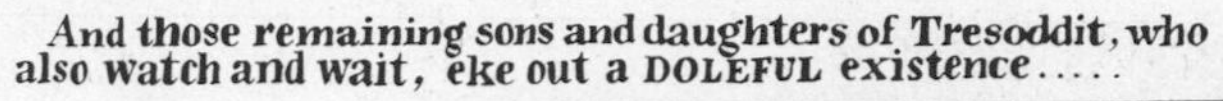
And those remaining sons and daughters of Tresoddit, who also watch and wait, eke out a DOLEFUL existence.....

The streets are silent....

...*and* the hostelries; bereft of regulars...*oilskinned, sea-booted, filling* the bar with salty chat....

....Only the wind howls....down the chimneys of all those depleted hearths: ..."*Crab Pots*"..."*Thrift Cottage*"..."*Everholme*"..."*Trunnions*"...

..."*Ocean Spray*"..

And then, one bright day, the *first* sail is spotted:

Soon, the fleet blows in to its haven.... for a *sojourn*, which *must* be all too brief.

But for a short while, the streets are full of merry mariners...and all the tills ring......

One Man's Meat...

How fortunate the *Webers* are in having friends with country cottages. This Easter, they're staying with *Pippa & Hamish*. And *what* a comfy cottage... almost *a home from home!*

Delicious Camembert, Pippa... buy it locally?
God, no!
Can't get that sort of thing round **HERE!** We have to bring almost everything with us....

People here... **CAN'T** tell you what they live on!
Most part, absolute **CRAP!**

Well, I s'ppose so many of them are out of work...
Yes, they are
But you should **SEE** the sort of expensive stuff they waste their money on!
ALL convenience food! **FULL** of chemicals and **SUGAR!**

You should **SEE** their super market baskets! ....well, it's the same in **town**, as well, I've noticed ...haven't you, Wendy?

Sausages... instant **soup**... **horrid**, synthetic toppings.. **NOTHING** fresh! ...... I mean, if I didn't have much money, I could still eat *frightfully* well!

They don't seem to have *heard* of casseroles....
But they can only afford to **HEAT**, not **COOK**
Meat's expensive
BONES aren't!

All kinds of *wonderful* **BONES** you can get at the butchers... **BOIL** them up... lovely **STOCK**...
...throw in a few *odds and ends*.... whizz them up in the blender...
Lots of lovely, lovely SOUP!

...Or, what about **PASTA!** Costs **nothing!** If you're broke, have it like the *Italian peasants* do.... ..little **garlic, olive oil,** tiny bit of parsley... **LOVELY!**

...or.. save money on fuel, eat raw things... **crudités**... **I adore** crudités.... whizz up a little *aioli*... **DELICIOUS!**
But vegetables are expensive!

Dandelions aren't!
There're *lovely* dandelions at the moment! We've eaten lots of ours in salads, recently
They're **so** good!

Anyway, not **ALL** veg. is expensive... What about **curly kale**? That's what people should eat...

Course, you **must** blanch it first... cook it a bit... *then* refresh it in cold water..... then re-heat it in butter.... **Delicious!** Little salt and black pepper.....
CHECK OUT
In other words, she means...
Let them eat **KALE**.

Up & Down the Country

Um...I'd like to **clear up** a few misunderstandings and **shed** a **TINY** bit of **LIGHT** on the work of **P.O.S.H**... the *Society for the* **Preservation** *of* **Owners** *of* *Second Homes*...

P.O.S.H. is a broad-based society...but we **DO** actually have to ***restrict*** membership to ***those second home owners***, who've taken ***on board*** the ***delicate*** moral position of the **dual home** situation....um...

..um..I **do** realise that in this day and age, **TWO** homes might seem on the surface, a ***tiny*** bit sort of ***IFFY***....

...but this is to ignore the **WIDELY** under-estimated **SERVICE** our membership performs, up and down the country....

..All over the country, our members have dipped into their pockets, in the cause of ***rural renewal*****.....**
Oh, you've made it so super, Guy!
Never believe it was a condemned cottage, this time last year, would you?

...They have renovated ***literally*** **THOUSANDS** of run-down, derelict properties....

..and breathed ***new life*** into old ***stables, barns, brewhouses, forges, mills, gutting sheds*** and ***chapels***....

:..thus ***transforming*** the **HOUSING STOCK** to meet future needs...an important contribution, when you consider, that...as ***Information*** and ***Communication Technology*** - fibre optics & so on - ..expands,...more people will live and work in the country....

Our members pay the **rates**.... but use the services infrequently. .....They help keep the roads in good repair...and do a useful job in keeping the *footpaths* open....

..They give the indigenous locals a proper sense of their own **ROOTS**...
Bludy week-enders!

Most **P.O.S.H.** members would *sincerely* like to live in the country, full-time....
Yes, REALLY, we ***WOULD*** live here..if it weren't for the kids' schooling...
And my job...

In **TOWN**, our members keep an exceptionally **LOW** and **DISCREET** profile....
You **NEVER** see them here at WEEKENDS...

:SOTTO VOCE: *They've got a* ***SECOND HOME!*** I've seen **him!**...trying to hide the hedge-cutters and the ***green WELLIES*** in the car boot!
!

So, if **YOU** have a member, or members of **P.O.S.H.** in your neighbourhood... **DO** remember..they **ARE** a force for **GOOD**... *Please be* **nice** to them...

Please!

Flattery
1. Physical World:
At a party, a lady meets an actor, star of the recent T.V. serial, "Wings over Walberswick," (the love story of a USAF pilot, stationed at Lakenheath, and the CND-activist warden of a bird sanctuary.), adapted from the novel by J.D. Crouch.
Oh god, I know people must say this to you MILLIONS of times ... but I thought you were WONDERFUL!
How very kind...
Thankyou
You were so GOOD!
You were just how I imagined Woody!
You really brought the book to life!
er..thanks.. ..I..er..
That scene in the bird hide with whatsername....
That's..um..very nice..um thank you...
..you brought it off BRILLIANTLY
I couldn't take my eyes off you!
You've got terrific PRESENCE! Are you a Leo, by any chance?
er..yes, I am...
There! I knew it! How Fascinating!
See, you've got all that lovely Leo Fire... AND so sensitive! I think you may have your MOON in Virgo....
Perhaps a Scorpio ascendant?.. Am I right?
I wouldn't know.
Me, I'm old ARIES... very Mars... but lots of Venus too!
Let me just...
Do let me do your chart sometime..it'd be such fun.. I'll give you my phone number..are Tuesday evenings any good? What about next week?
Excuse me I must just find the loo.
People must say this to you all the time, but I did think you were MARVELLOUS...
How kind
2. Animal Level:
Leo ♌
Aries ♈
Flatter... Flatter... ..Wonderful! ..Flatter... Noble!... flatter..
Ooh! That's nice! Mmm!
Ooh... little bit more! ooh! lovely!
flatter... ..flatter... Brilliant! flatter... super!
ooh! Enough! enough!
Flatter flatter..
OK... now can the sheep lie down with the lion?
What!
Certainly not!
It gets you nowhere.
3. Symbolic Coda:
Aries
Leo
You're WONDERFUL! BRILLIANT! Terrific!
thank you...
You're DIVINE! MARVELLOUS! SO TALENTED!
How kind
sorry
©Posy Simmonds 1982

Spring Fever
Some things are perpetual, amaranthine... NEVER changing: Since the Dawn of Time, SPRING has wrought a pretty havoc... unsealing the buds, scattering the moist meadows with flowers, filling shy places with the chestnut blooms of the Hairy Woodrush (luzula pilosa).....
Spring has always fired the blood.. has always made wanton demands.....
Prithee, why not?
Pray unhand me... I'd rather be DEAD!
...upon Virtue, Modesty & Honour (and their attendant double standards).
This Spring, it is Julian Heep (18) whose fancy has lightly turned to thoughts of Love
Look, Helene, Why NOT? Gimme 2 good reasons...
I just don't want to, that's all
That's not a reason! You don't like me... that it?
Nuh..
WHAT then!?!
Why NOT?
Just, lay OFF, Julian!
You're on the PILL.. you can't be scared, so WHY?!
I told you... I just don't want to.....
If you don't want to, why you on the Pill, then, eh? Tell me
Look, Helene, everyone else does it....
Oh yeah! I know everyone else does...& then everyone else BRAGS to his mates at school, afterwards, don't they?
...and then everyone else's mates call the girls that DO, SLAGS...
..and the ones that DON'T, Teases & lezzies...
Well, you did lead me on, didn't you?
I bloody DIDN'T!
You asked me to help with your Maths!
Same old story!

Married Persons' Guide to LUNCHING
1. Luncheon Invitation:
Tell you what.. why don't you & I have lunch next week?
Your husband won't mind, will he?
No, no
That would be nice..
2. Heavy Lunch:
When can we do this again?
3. funny-Business Lunch:
Where shall we go, Friday? ...somewhere quiet...hmm... ...just you & me...
Mmm
Chez Marcel
4. Déjeuner sur l'Herbe: (Naked Lunch)
I was just thinking.... normally I ADORE wet grass...but next time, maybe we try a MOTEL...
5. Naked Lunch Box:
Tuna fish or ham on rye?
MOTEL
6. Skipped Lunch:
I've got to get back at 3·00... ....what d'you say we SKIP lunch and go straight to the..uh... motel?
erm...
7. Late Lunch:
Look, I've been waiting over an HOUR!! It's the second time!
I said I wasn't sure I could today.....
..and please don't call me at the office
8. Lunch Break:
I just can't go on like this any more
...I just feel it's really got kind of... ROUTINE...
It's like we don't seem to communicate...
OK, if that's the way you...
Anyway, my husband's beginning to sus-pect.....
9. Ladies' Luncheon:
...then, suddenly it was as if he'd had this total personality transplant.... bastard began treating me like a... surrogate MEAL!
Creep! Louse! Who needs that!
SICILIA
Posy Simmonds 1982

But *this* month, his car is a **Torture Chamber**...and Stanhope has joined that *secret society,* which passes a *mauvais quart d'heure,* each evening, after the hours of business....

...Discreetly parked, racked and pinioned in the *crumple zone,* Stanhope endures *Brief Encounters* of sniffs and sighs and recriminations.....

Killjoy was here....
Taxi!

Here is Stanhope Wright at London Airport, positively bursting with sap, fresh from the slopes of St Hérisson....
Well, I don't have to take 'em, guv, but I will..if you can get 'em in...
That's very civil of you!

Nice TAN... Been away?
Oh.. few days skiing... just a QUICKIE....

Just nipped orf, did you?
Well... I did have a little business in Geneva... but that only took a day....
..and I had a little gap in my... DIARY... so I thought: WHY NOT? Office can look after itself...

That's the way! ALL for it! Got to enjoy yourself when you can, haven't you?!
Oh YES!
I mean, no one's going to do it for you, are they?
No No They're not!

All work and no play, eh? Got to look after Number 1, haven't we?
Oh, we have!

Specially these days... no good letting things pass you by, is it?
No, no, it's not!

Not all we want, Life, is it?
No, it's not
But it's all we got...
True...true...

..So, we got to make the best of it
Absolutely!

Gor! You're a real TONIC, you are! ...first punter I've had in weeks with a smile on the dial!
Ah...

Glad SOMEONE's got something to smile about...makes a change, I
Sorry?

I said...you look very pleased with life... RARE thing... what with the country up the spout...millions on the breadline...
What?

...total state of economic collapse.... GLOOM... DESPAIR...
Look, I don't want you to think I....

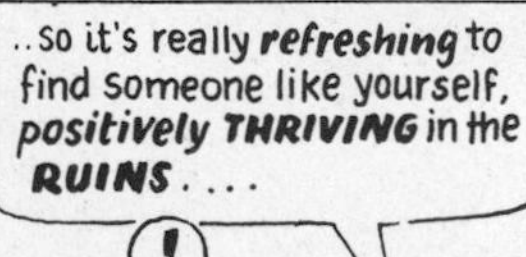

..so it's really refreshing to find someone like yourself, positively THRIVING in the RUINS....

!

Still... always a FEW fiddling while Rome burns, aren't there?... stands to reason....

It's an ill wind, innit?

You still there, guv?

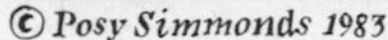

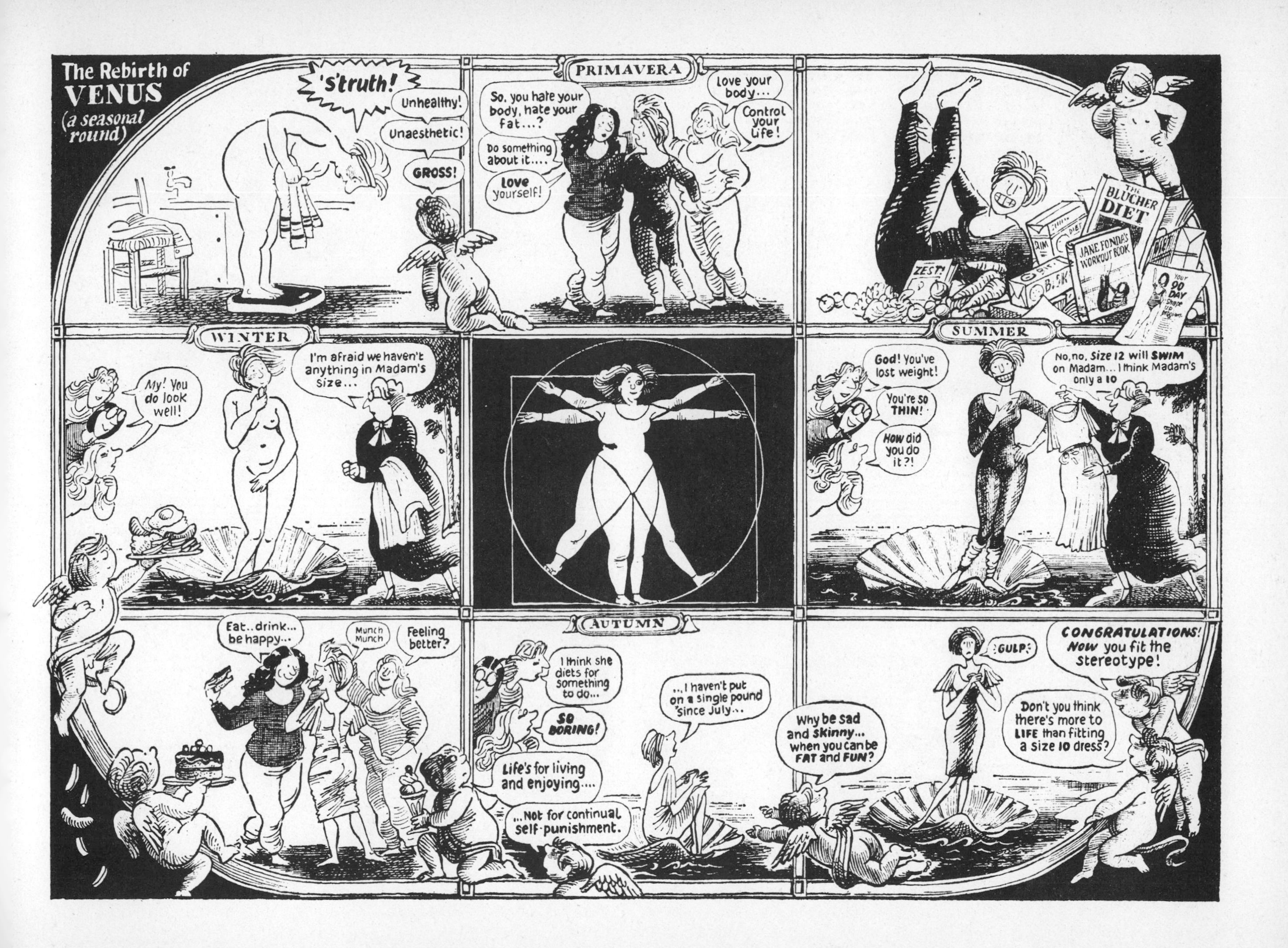

The Rebirth of VENUS (a seasonal round)
's'truth!
Unhealthy!
Unaesthetic!
GROSS!
PRIMAVERA
So, you hate your body, hate your fat...?
Do something about it....
Love yourself!
Love your body...
Control your life!
THE BLUCHER DIET
JANE FONDA'S WORKOUT BOOK
ZEST!
WINTER
My! You do look well!
I'm afraid we haven't anything in Madam's size...
SUMMER
God! You've lost weight!
You're so THIN!
How did you do it?!
No, no, Size 12 will SWIM on Madam... I think Madam's only a 10
Eat.. drink... be happy...
Munch Munch
Feeling better?
AUTUMN
I think she diets for something to do...
SO BORING!
Life's for living and enjoying....
...Not for continual self-punishment.
...I haven't put on a single pound since July...
Why be sad and skinny... when you can be FAT and FUN?
GULP
CONGRATULATIONS! Now you fit the stereotype!
Don't you think there's more to LIFE than fitting a size 10 dress?

Little Kate's birthday party..... In the kitchen, parents have gathered to watch its final throes......

If we see the gestures encoded as a non-linguistic symbolic system... in a state of unlimited semiosis, forming... er.. an open text, which we perceive.. ONLY as a series of MICRO-PROPOSITIONAL utterances, with infinitive possibilities of meaning....

A SUPER WOMAN'S DAY.....
CORN PUFFS
The Commanding Business Woman
The Provident Housewife
The Commanding Business Woman
The Welcoming Mother
PUFF PUFF
The Angel of the Hearth
PUFF PANT
PUFF PUFF PUFF PANT
PUFF PUFF
PUFF PUFF PUFF
The Strumpet of the Boudoir
GROAN

Standards of Living

It's the first time that Benji Weber has been left at a certain friend's house, while Wendy attends a lecture....
It is good of you, Laura..
That's OK, Wendy

Later, Wendy & her mother pick Benji up...
Bye!

That Laura's a sweet thing... and very obliging... but..... are you thinking what I'm thinking, Wendy?
Mmn

Yes... well, I'm afraid I didn't find Laura's ... quite... er... comme il faut.....

...NOT ideal for Benji, did you think?
No, not really

' Tell the truth, looking round there.... I nearly absolutely had FORTY FITS!!

I thought it was GHASTLY!

Not a place to leave a child... do you?
Well.... perhaps not

O I AM relieved, darling! I'm sure you'll find some one else... but I couldn't relax for a minute, if I knew Benji was going there again!

There were things there to CURDLE your blood!
Yes, there was something...

NODDY IN TOYLAND
Those awful stairs! That unguarded fire! That frayed electric cord! Awful old nappies lying about! The bleach bottle! That great carving knife! Soiled tea cloths! Rucked-up rug! Cat litter all over the place...!

Yes.... that Noddy book!

Charity ... begins at Home

Almost every morning, Gemma *used* to kiss her *smashing* husband and go out of her *lovely* house to her *super* job...

... leaving her two, little chicks (one of nursery age, one in the nest), safe in the care of her *wonderful* Nanny, Anita.

And almost every day, Gemma would marvel at her *immense* good fortune at being able to combine *Career* and *Motherhood* so easily:

On Anita's day off, Gemma would go to pick up Katie from nursery school and some of the other parents would comment on her enviable arrangement...

Some of them would tell Gemma their own organisational *horror stories*:

Then, one day, some of the mothers, singly & severally, wondered if they might have a quick *word* with Gemma....

And *NOW* every morning, Gemma goes out of her *lovely* house to her *super job*, leaving her 2 little chicks & Carol-opposite's Dominic & Baby Clarke & often Tessa Campion's Sara & little Alec, while Alice goes to the dentist...& Benji Weber, while Wendy has a lecture.... ALL safe in the care of Gemma's *wonderful* Nanny, Anita...

...and Gemma *feels absolutely* pis off up here!

An acceptable LIE
Barry Pimlott rang.........
...Jennifer Cole's Personal Assistant...
at Walmer & Wilcox (Publishers) Ltd....
He said to her....
...She said to him......
...The Consequence was........
...and The World said.....
Hello...Ya?
Can I speak to Jennifer Cole, please?
Frightfully sorry... she still isn't back from lunch....
Oh. Oh, I see... right, fine..thanks
As Business Folk, we know full well, That lunch may last a lengthy spell...
An acceptable LIE
Mary Truscott rang.........
...Jennifer Cole's Personal Assistant...
at Walmer & Wilcox (Publishers) Ltd....
She said to her.....
...She said to her.....
...The Consequence was......
...and The World said......
Hello...Ya?
Can I speak to Jennifer Cole, please?
Frightfully sorry.... She's in a meeting all day....
Oh... Oh, I see... right, fine, thanks.
As Business Folk, we know it's true... Meetings can last the whole day through
An acceptable LIE
Harry Wetlock rang.........
...Jennifer Cole's Personal Assistant...
at Walmer & Wilcox (Publishers) Ltd.....
He said to her.....
...She said to him......
...The Consequence was.....
...and The World said......
Hello..Ya?
Can I speak to Jennifer Cole, please?
Frightfully sorry... She's not in today... Her car broke down...
Oh dear! I see... ..right, fine... thanks
As Business Folk, we're of one Accord... A man is lost without his Ford....
The unacceptable TRUTH
Larry Diplock rang........
...Jennifer Cole's Personal Assistant
..at Walmer & Wilcox (Publishers) Ltd
He said to her.....
...She said to him.....
Hello...Ya?
Can I speak to Jennifer Cole ?
Frightfully sorry.... she's not in today.... School holidays...she's looking after her kids..
LOOKING after her KIDS??!! Bloody Hell, what kind of excuse is that?!!!
...and The World said.......
We all agree! He's not alone! Domestic cares should be left at Home!
..and Jennifer Cole said:
As Business Folk, You now know why Us Working Mums Are bound to lie!
© Posy Simmonds 1985

Waiting for Mummy...

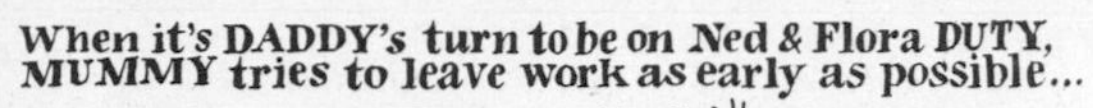

When it's DADDY's turn to be on Ned & Flora DUTY, MUMMY tries to leave work as early as possible...

Look... I drawed a sausage...
Lovely, darling...
Look!

CLICK CLICK!
Mum!

Hallo, darling! Did you have a nice day?
I done drawins

Who's been a good girl all day! Been drawing? HOW LOVELY! What a good, good girl!

BWAAA!

Oh, NED!
Baba!

What's all dis, den? How's mummy's lovely baba, den? Is oos a good boy?
Goo!

Are you? Are you lovely? Are you a lovely baba?

Mum!
MUM!

Let's sit down ...... oof...
Then I can talk to both of you...
There!

SIGH!

Oh DARLING!

Oh Philip! Poor neglected man!....

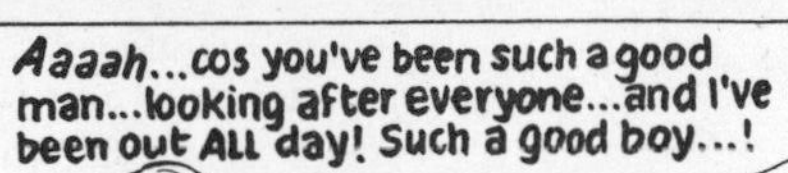

Aaaah...cos you've been such a good man...looking after everyone...and I've been out ALL day! Such a good boy...!

Meroow!

Oh PUSSY! Poor, neglected pussy..!
Meerow!

You wait your turn, like everyone else!

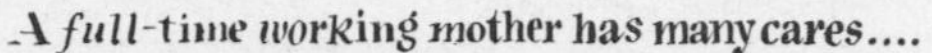

...but however *wearing* the week at work....

...*however* great the desire for *peace & quiet*..the children's *social life* comes first....

Here is a local taxi returning *George Weber*, his *Family Rail Card* & some of his children, to the station, after *Half Term* spent in Tresoddit....

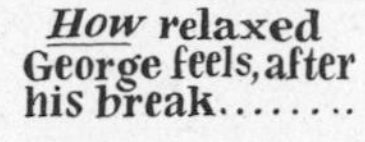

How relaxed George feels, after his break........

...this long, carefree weekend of Discovery: *sea shells..conkers ...edible funghi..crispy leaves...*

...and *now*... a crispy *tenner*, down the side of the back seat....

......which impales George on the horns of a dilemma:–

Birth of the Blues
What a lot of visitors come to greet the new addition to a family...!
My God, he's big! Looks a real bruiser!
Lovely hair!
Wasted on a boy, of course ... pity Saskia hasn't... ooh, just look at those eye-lashes!
Aren't you a lucky girl to have such a nice baby brother!
Oh how SWEET of you, Wendy!
Rather coals to Newcastle ..but you can't have too many!
No, darling, I don't think Baby likes being poked, do you!
I'll knit him a nice little pilch, next...
No..we don't shine the torch on him, Saskia..not a good idea...
Oh! And how SWEET of you, Aunt Bea!
...and isn't he lucky to have a nice big sister like you!
Don't think he likes Lego, yet, Saskia...
She's very intrigued by him, that one... Doesn't seem to be jealous, thank God.
It's always tricky at first, isn't it?
Oh a woolly hedgehog! How killing!
And here's a little something for Saskia...
O, I say, that is sweet of you, Wendy!
What do we say, Saskia?
eh?
eh?
Haven't we forgotten something, Saskia!?
Well, Wendy better take it back... I don't think little girls deserve presents, if they don't say...
Fankyou..
That's better!
O... Happy Families! How lovely!
And what d'you say to your Mummie and Daddie for giving you such a nice baby brother?
eh?
eh?
If you don't say thank you....usually they take it away....

Aaah... but she's gorgeous!
It is visiting time in a maternity ward....
Oh she's lovely!
SHAME you didn't have a boy...
Ah well..better luck next time...Aaah! But she's gorgeous!
What about John? Does he mind?
Well, I think he would have liked a boy...
Aaaaah he wanted a boy..'course he did!
Aah but she's lovely!
But isn't he BIG, Sue! Great, tough chap!
Oh, he's heaven!
Spitting image of you, Ian!
Very sweet, tho..
...Still, there's plenty of time, isn't there? P'raps you'll have a boy next time....
Honestly, I didn't mind what I had, as long as it was healthy... I'm THRILLED with her!
'Course you are!
Oh yes! Girls are just as nice!
Oh no! We wouldn't swop you now, would we, my precious!
NICER to have a boy first, though, isn't it?!
Aaah... but she's lovely!
Happiness!
Congratulations!
on the new arrival!
IT'S A GIRL!
Here's a special birthday greeting
to tell you of our joy....
You're ev'ry bit as wanted, dear,
As if you'd been a BOY!
We mustn't make distinctions now....
GIRLS are just as good and true
You march alongside boys thru Life
And fight the battles too!
Your rôle is just as vital
In love and peace and war....
...Tho' BOYS are officers in Life's Guards
And GIRLS the Catering Corps!

Mother's Quiet Time
BABA'S
Prune Yogurt Surprise

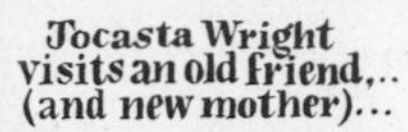
Jocasta Wright visits an old friend,... (and new mother)...

Hi Jocasta

BWAAAAAAA!!
Oh God! Not again!
What's the matter with it... I mean, *him*?
NuGGies
Mother & Baby
Parent

Nothing.. he just *yells* all the time... ...at the clinic, they say "*What lovely* healthy lungs he's got..."
Parent

They say I should leave him to *squawk* a bit... but I *can't!* The neighbours go *barking* mad....
BWAAAAAA!!

'Praps he's got a *pin* sticking in him.
Time for Toofy-bix

He doesn't have *pins*..he's in *disposables*...and he's not *wet*..just looked...
WAAAAAA!!

And he hasn't got *colic* or *wind*....
No more Nappy rash!
Your letters

..he isn't *teething* or *constipated*...
New Baba-Dins.. helping him grow...

And he just spat this lot back at me...so he's not *hungry!*

Waaa!

I've picked him up...rocked him, cuddled him, soothed him... played with him... ...tired him out...
Ssh...
All's quiet...thanks to

I've done *everything* they say you should...
Oh God... SIGH
Poor you...
Your Baby Month by

WAHaaAA! WAAAAA!!
Strugglers
Strugglers
Mother & Right Little SOD
New! GOB-IT-BACK BABY DINNERS

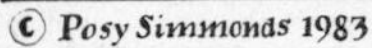

PUBLIC VIEW

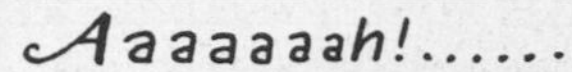

. . . Oh.... Oh dear!...... *no, no, no!* ... **not** at **TABLE!**

Oh **NO!** .. in the **OFFICE!**.... No, no, no!

. . . Oh **really!** **No!**

No, no! That child's **MUCH** too old to be breast fed!

Oh dear. . . a baby with a **DUMMY**. . .

Aah... BOTTLE-FED.. Jolly good second-best.... (Breast is best!)

The Milk of Human Kindness

The Weber Family enter a newsagents in search of ice cream for its younger members.

Accompanying them is American *ethno-botanist*, Frisbee Summers, (currently on sabbatical from the *Perceptronics Division* of a Communications Multi National.).......

G.D.

While negotiations progress, Frisbee examines the upper shelves...

Monkey Business.

Some of the Weber family are visiting the Zoo. Here they are, finally, in the Monkey House....

But what dey doing, vose monkeys?
GRANNEE! What are they doing?

What's dat pink fing?
What is it?
Well, I can't quite..... I haven't got my right specs, darling... I expect it's his tail, don't you?
No it's not!

Yes, well, let's look at the next ones, shall we, darlings?
But why do they do that?

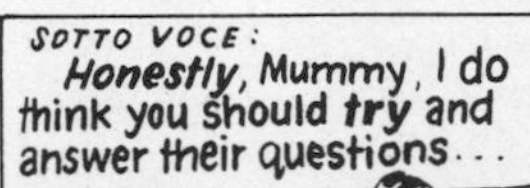
SOTTO VOCE:
Honestly, Mummy, I do think you should try and answer their questions...

Well, it's SO EMBARASSING, Wendy!

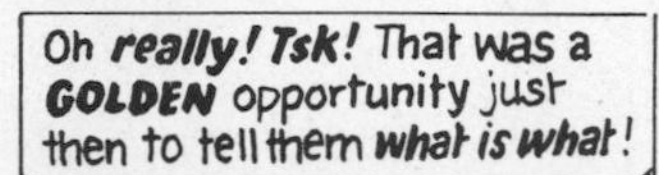
Oh really! Tsk! That was a GOLDEN opportunity just then to tell them what is what!

They know a certain amount already...
Just simple answers.... nothing too complicated....

I just think it's terribly important to tell them things when they ask....

And I don't want them thinking there's something nasty & unmentionable about SEX....
But they are a bit young...

Mummy, why's its bottom all pink?

Why is it?
Tell us!
Why is...
What is it?
What is that?
Tell me..
Now listen...

sort of signal
blah blah swelling
blah blah
girl monkeys

courtship
Daddy monkeys
mating
blah blah babies blah blah

blah
blah

TABOO

Here are the Weber family at Wendy's sister's, celebrating Aunt Bunny's 80th birthday.....

It's cheese fondue, Aunt Bunny.....
Oh.. how QUEER it looks
Where's Sophie got to?
I don't know

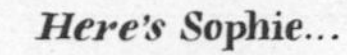

Here's Sophie...

Oh... there you are!

Whisper Whisper!

O, yes, I like cheese.. I'm what you might call a "cheesy person"...
O good!

What about a little mustard, Belinda?
No thanks

Fondue? Would that be a Hindoo sort of word?
It's French, Bunny...

..and this stuff's fine for drinking every day...
You MUST remember that two-piece... pink and white...
I DO I do!

..so we thought we'd knock down that wall & make a playroom...
No, I haven't seen HER in YEARS!
Shall I get some pudding?
Can I get down?

Bye Bye!
OK, Soph?

You SAID, Mum.. You SAID!!!
What?

.. When we had our private TALK!... ..about it NOT being a curse.. you SAID it would be something to celebrate, when it started..something important! NOT something to ignore.. you said it was NORMAL and NATURAL!! WHY you so embarrassed?! Why'd you all whisper? Why..?
Well, darling, it wasn't quite the right ti..
Eh?
Well when is the right time!?

Whisper
Now, have we time for Racing Demon before you go?

Useful Occupation
Ring!
Ring!

Oh, Jane, dear... how did you get on?

You didn't get it?...Oh! I'm sorry....Over 600 applicants? Oh dear! And your 12th interview, I know......
Poor you!

I suppose it's the recession
What do I mean?
Well, p'raps they think the jobs shouldn't go to a MARRIED WOMAN. After all, you have got a family, dear...

Look, don't shout dear!... I know the children are practically grown up......

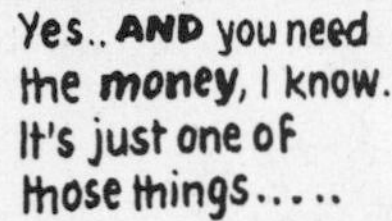

Yes.. AND you need the money, I know. It's just one of those things.....
What, dear?

What are you supposed to do all day for the next 40 years? I don't know, dear... at least you'll have time to do it all properly...get ALL the egg off the forks...
I was only joking, Jane..

Well, what about voluntary work?
The cutbacks have affected...
What?
Don't SHOUT, dear, I know the State reneged on lots of its responsibilities....

Cheer up, Jane, it could be worse

...you'll find something to do... look at me... I did...and, after all, with your father, there wasn't even any QUESTION of my going out to work... things were different then...... One can keep oneself busy, what with one thing and another!
All right, dear... bye bye...

Now, where was I? Oh, yes...

Now, Laurence, what d'you think I'm going to needlepoint for you next, eh? A book mark? Another cummerbund?
A pocket calculator cover?
Bless our Home
Evening

Don't Know

Z Z Z z

MALTBY
Wright
Davis

R-ring!
Z...

?

SCRATCH
SCRATCH

Crackers

Yeah?

Oh, Good day to you....
Miss Wright ?
Yeah

I can count on your support for
Ron Baker on June 9th, can I ?
Yeah

Oh good! And would you like one of these
to stick in your window ?
Yeah
Thank you!
VOTE
RON BAKER
LABOUR

LABOUR

LABOUR
CRACKLE

VOTE
SMITH
SDP
LABOUR
VOTE
BRIGGS
PALMER

VOTE
SMITH
SDP
LABOUR

Z Z Z
VOTE
SMITH
SDP
VOTE
BRIGGS
CONSERVATIVE

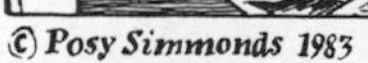

SLOTH

A NEW VICTORIAN VIRTUE:

In these troubled times, let us praise Sloth...for, do we not perceive that, where the Spirit of Slothfulness is absent, how The Suffering Multitude FRETS & roars & clutches in vain after the coat tails of the Tyrant, WORK?

But, where Sloth dwells, then there must recline Docile Citizens, the unobtrusive recipients of National Benevolence.

The Suffering Multitude

The Docile Citizen

THE IMPORTANCE *of* SLOTHFULNESS:

Sloth subdues the Refractory Tendencies in Humanity, & discourages the Habit of Industry & brings to the Disorderly, the Balm of Peace.

Let us embrace Sloth! And promote that Virtue, & seek that admirable felicity of taste which finds Meaning in Enforced Idleness!

Let the sage father accustom his sons to a life of inactivity, and his daughters to bask in infinite domesticity.

For it is far better to GIVE UP and RECEIVE.

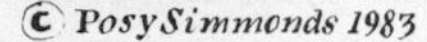

Medical Precautions

SURGERY
Measles
NO SMOKING

Jocasta Wright...

Yes...er...Miss Wright... what **seems** to be the trouble....?

Um ... like... see... when I pee ... sort of

yes ... bladder... ... passing water?

Yes, well, I think we'll take a look, shall we?...Just slip off your stockings & whatnot, would you?
...and **hop** up on the couch over there....

That's it! **Magic!**...Now, would you mind if my assistant, Mrs **Toser** stands outside the door, while I examine you?
What?

My assistant, Mrs Toser, will be outside the door, while I examine you...
Oh that's **OK**, Doctor...no **need**, really...I'm not worried... I mean...you wouldn't **TRY ANYTHING**, would you, I mean....

SEETHE SEETHE

CHEEKY little..!!!!

I don't think you **QUITE** understand, Miss Wright....
Mrs Toser's there more for **MY** protection, than **yours**....

YOUR protection!

SEETHE
BLOODY cheek!!

Daily Thing
GIRL KNEES G.P.'s NOSE HORROR!
Daily Other
G.P. ADMINISTERS SPANKING, HORROR
Provoked: "THE THINGS I HAVE TO PUT UP WITH FROM PATIENTS"

Upright Citizens
Bensons
STOP
35 414 28
We're often obliged to hang about in Life....
Oh my poor feet, Wendy!
Wretched service!
You know, we've been here 25 minutes!!
Tsk!
Then you get 3 buses all together!
Geroff!
YAWN
...But it's one of Life's trifling inequalities....
Ooh My feet!
..when you think how good the buses used to be...
Yees... crying shame! Stands to reason, doesn't it?
When's this sodding bus coming, then?
...that the young can at least SIT out an interminable wait....
....without looking out of the ordinary....
...But those of riper years...
(some of whom are dying to take the weight off their feet...)
....will risk being taken for a serious casualty of urban infrastructural decay....
SOCIETY TODAY
This week:
The Uncaring Society:
Vagrancy & the Poverty Trap.
N. Pittwell
Photographs by
Eric Fawley

All the Ward's a Stage, And all the patients merely players: They have their exits and their entrances; And one patient in her time plays many parts:

First she plays a **WOMAN of forty**, *with a suitcase, having a minor operation....*

...then she becomes an **INFANT**, *mewling behind a paperback.....*

Then she has a small speaking rôle:

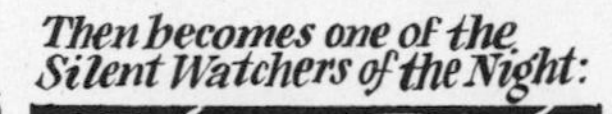

Then becomes one of the Silent Watchers of the Night:

Next, a larger part..that of a **DOZY FLY** *in winter.........*

Then a **CHILD**:

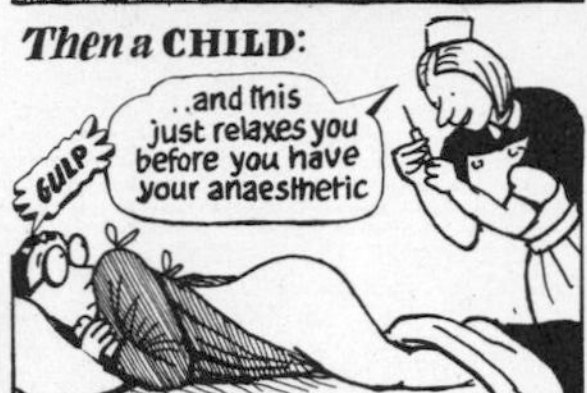

..And then... **LIME-LIT** *in surgical green, she plays the part of* **LEADING LADY**:

Next, a plum rôle of **WOUNDED SOLDIER**, *returned from the front, sighing in a bower...*

Then a try for the part of **PALE HANDS** *playing on a coverlet....*

Finally, a small walk-off part:

Reaction
Just when you were thinking that Sensibility had entirely atrophied in the young.....
Oh wow! He looks really weird decapitated!
Yeah!
(Remembering that these are the same little chicks who once wept at "Mary Poppins"...
It's all right, Muffy...it's only a film...
SOB
..who were unconsolable when the gerbils died....
Oh Mommy! Poor, poor, poor liddle things!
... but who are now the unflinching Connoisseurs of all Horror, Torture, Carnage...)
Yeah, an' remember that bit where they tie him down an' the giant ants eat his stomach!
Oh yeah! Really great!
and the bit with the red hot poker!
... Just when you were really despairing.....
You watch...you see this guy jump from the 12th floor & go S-P-L-A-T! on the sidewalk!
Wow!
...they reveal an underlayer of délicatesse:
Oh NO!
Turn it OFF!
Hey that's GROSS!
Gaad! I can't look!
!
God! Patrick, the kids are actually REVOLTED by something on T.V!
Whaat!
Something on the NEWS...
?
Gaad! GROSS! Wanna throw up!
Eeuuch!!
Bleuch!
Well, it's a guy reporting on a violent break-in.. I mean, I guess that is kind of upsetting, but....
Oh Gaad, Dad! Not the break-in... take a look at the reporter, if you can stand it... he's wearing BELL BOTTOMS!!! Bleuuch!!
An'a SAFARI SUIT!!!... in polyester double-knit! Eaeruch!
Oh NO!!
Blaaach!
PLATFORM SOLES!! I can't bear it! MEDALLIONS! CHEST HAIR!!
contrasting SADDLE STICHING!!
© Posy Simmonds

Judicium Extremum
(The LAST Judgement)
Mundus
World
Bellum
War
Homines in aërem ejiciuntur, vel exuruntur.... terribile est!
Men are blown up into the air, or are burnt.... it is terrible!
BAN ALL NUCLEAR WEAPONS!
Nuclear weapons were provocative!
Nuclear weapons acted as a deterrent!
DEPLOY CRUISE NOW!
Next!
All your fault! You left us DEFENCELESS!
Your bloody fault! Your lot made us into a TARGET!
We told you this would happen!
We told you this would happen, all along!
We wouldn't be here, if we'd all scrapped the lot!
NO CRUISE MISSI
It's all your fault!
It's all YOUR fault!
HAWKS Q
Next!
DOVES
DOVES Q
© Posy Simmonds 1983

FLY'S Undoing
Here is a business meeting reaching a natural break....
So... I think we could leave it there, gentlemen..... ...passed nem. diss....
The laboratory facility... could you just recap on the bottom line?
That went rather well! Even managed to win over old Mills....
Congratulations! Well, that went very well, Julia
Hear Hear
Oh thanks, Derek... well, see you in a few minutes
Must have a Jimmy Riddle...
Me too
MEN
Yes.... I HAVE won them over
But for how long? I don't trust Derek.
He gets them all in the GENTS, and mounts a rearguard action.....
God! WISH I could be a FLY on the wall for ten minutes!
You SHALL be a FLY on the wall for ten minutes!
I am a fairy godmother! You SHALL go to the GENTS!
!
Oh, now come on, Derek!
Look.. we can easily change that decision... ...pass a resolution to do the opposite...
!!!
Seems a bit...
Ah, come on! It's not what we really wanted.. I can fix Julia, tough cookie, Though she is....
Tsk! These BOSSY women! Royal pains!
They need slapping down a bit...
BUZZ*!*⚡*!!
What was that?
Some sort of BUG!
...that lives to fight another day....

In the offices of International Brewhouse Incorporated....

DISTINGUISHED PREVARICATION MEDAL

 R.T.S.

E.C.

At the Poly, the term progresses... the Departmental notice board is in full *leaf*.... Today, *GEORGE WEBER (Senior Lecturer in Liberal Studies)*, is struck by a recent addition.....

Hey! Have you seen this?

What?

Oh, I had one in my pigeon hole...

"The attention of all members of staff is called to the decision of the school management committee at its meeting on 14 Nov. 1981, which ratified the earlier decision of the Faculty Board, to DENY access to ALL PERSONS other than APPROVED VISITORS.

The reasons for this decision are as follows:

1i The Education Authority is not responsible for, nor insured against, accidents which may happen to, or be occasioned by, UNAUTHORISED persons.

1ii Its guarantees in respect of CRIME prevention can no longer, in such circumstances, be sustained. (Instrument of Government para. 72, note iii)

2. The unsuitability of visitors' clothing may hazardise relations to various statutes. (Staff are referred to Ray Collins for clarification on this one.)

2.i The progress & development of the Faculty's links with local industry & commerce could be imperilled by an injudicious, apparent breach of the confidentiality implicit in such co-operative arrangements.

2.ii The DISTRACTION produced by the presence of visitors can prejudice the academic atmosphere of application and...

What the heck is **all this about?**

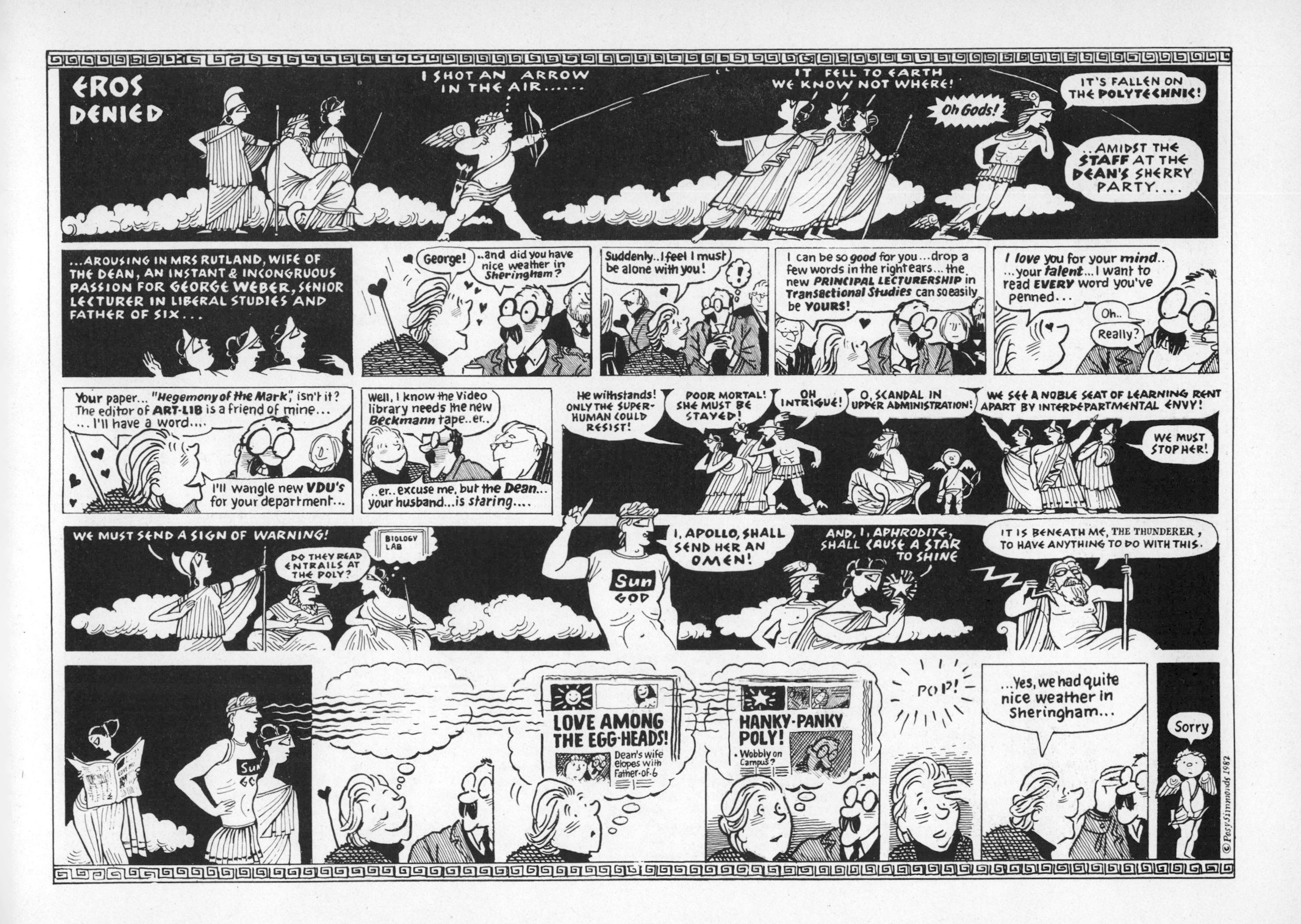

EROS DENIED
I SHOT AN ARROW IN THE AIR......
IT FELL TO EARTH WE KNOW NOT WHERE!
Oh Gods!
IT'S FALLEN ON THE POLYTECHNIC!
...AMIDST THE STAFF AT THE DEAN'S SHERRY PARTY....
...AROUSING IN MRS RUTLAND, WIFE OF THE DEAN, AN INSTANT & INCONGRUOUS PASSION FOR GEORGE WEBER, SENIOR LECTURER IN LIBERAL STUDIES AND FATHER OF SIX...
George!
..and did you have nice weather in Sheringham?
Suddenly..I feel I must be alone with you!
!
I can be so good for you...drop a few words in the right ears...the new PRINCIPAL LECTURERSHIP in Transactional Studies can so easily be YOURS!
I love you for your mind.. ...your talent...I want to read EVERY word you've penned...
Oh..
Really?
Your paper... "Hegemony of the Mark", isn't it? The editor of ART-LIB is a friend of mine... ...I'll have a word....
I'll wangle new VDU's for your department...
Well, I know the Video library needs the new Beckmann tape..er..
..er..excuse me, but the Dean... your husband...is staring....
He withstands! ONLY THE SUPER-HUMAN COULD RESIST!
POOR MORTAL! SHE MUST BE STAYED!
OH INTRIGUE!
O, SCANDAL IN UPPER ADMINISTRATION!
WE SEE A NOBLE SEAT OF LEARNING RENT APART BY INTERDEPARTMENTAL ENVY!
WE MUST STOP HER!
WE MUST SEND A SIGN OF WARNING!
DO THEY READ ENTRAILS AT THE POLY?
BIOLOGY LAB
I, APOLLO, SHALL SEND HER AN OMEN!
Sun GOD
AND, I, APHRODITE, SHALL CAUSE A STAR TO SHINE
IT IS BENEATH ME, THE THUNDERER, TO HAVE ANYTHING TO DO WITH THIS.
LOVE AMONG THE EGG-HEADS!
Dean's wife elopes with Father-of-6
HANKY-PANKY POLY!
• Wobbly on Campus?
POP!
...Yes, we had quite nice weather in Sheringham...
Sorry
© Posy Simmonds 1982

This is the house that Jack sold.....

This is the house that Jack wants.....

This is the chap that lives in the house that Jack wants.....

This is the price asked by the chap, that lives in the house that Jack wants....

God! That house!... It's perfect... perfect!

Right... we'll make him an offer.....

These are the solicitors, dressed in black.... (*One* for *Shite*, one for Jack).... ..who handle these things for a healthy whack......

Jack makes his offer without delay....

Shite's accepted!

Oh I SAY!!

...*And soon the deal is under way*......

This is the *surveyor*, friend of Jack's, who inspects Shite's house for rot and cracks.....

Here's Jack's contract in black and white.... *signed* by Jack, delivered to *Shite*:

But, *this* is the *berk* who made a NEW bid... (*a few thousand more quid*)....

...That scuppered the deal and stopped the cheque...

...... causing *Shite* to crow in the morn... and tell his lawyer *the hice had gorn*....

...who rang the solicitor dressed in black:

..who passed the message on to Jack....

..who *blasted* off a barrage of *flak*....

...and kicked the dog...

..and worried the cat

..and ate his hat....

...and part of a mat.....

Because, there they are in a short-let flat....

....to the dump of a house that Jack....

Lingua Franca
On their way home from school, Wendy & the children are offered a lift....
Hop in!
Tara, get in the back, there's a good girl...
O how **sweet** of you, Pippa!

How's Tara? Haven't seen you for a long time... **nice** being back at **school**, is it?
Budge up Benji!
OW!
'Haven't gone back yet.

Not **yet**? I thought everyone ha....
..er...Tara's **not** at **Fletcher-Montacute** anymore, Wendy... we...um...moved her...couple of terms ago...to...er...

..to..er.... a **PRIVATE** boarding school
!

Knew you'd be shocked, Wendy....**knew** you'd think us **traitors**...but **DO try** to understand..we were **very** worried about her at **Fletcher**...

That school's **so** enormous... honestly, Wendy, she seemed ...**overwhelmed**...never **quite** fitted in...

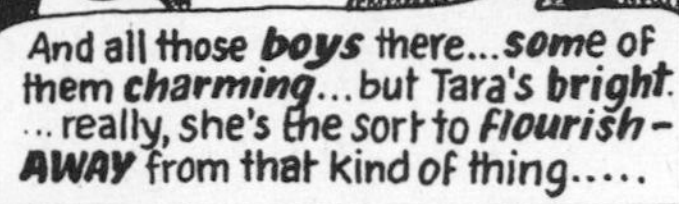
And all those **boys** there...**some** of them **charming**... but Tara's **bright**. ...really, she's the sort to **Flourish-AWAY** from that kind of thing.....

And I was **desperately** worried about her **ENGLISH**...
The way she spoke?
NO, no, no, no! NOT her **ACCENT**!...although they did all have rather ghastly **voices**..**no**, I mean her basic use of her native language.....

You **do** agree that's important, don't you, Wendy? And...you know me, I'm **all** for **Cultural mix**...but at **Fletcher**... there **DID** seem to be rather **more**, you know, **visibly** ethnic children than one might...er...

And at this **new** school, they're very **strong** on **English**...
They <u>have</u> to be!.....

My Boarding School:
My name is WEN YIN-YU. My father Hong Kong millionaire. I come here learn good English
My name is Maria Villanueva. I improve my English here
I am Miss Sulaiman from Oman.
My name's Sue Styles...my dad sent me here to learn to talk posh.
I am Agape Eleftheriou from Athens

SNOBS

Why can't I have one, Mum? 'Snot fair!
Darling, I'm NOT buying you a leather skirt costing £60! It's too much!
What is? I want one!

All my friends've got one! ... Laura... Emma... Stephanie!

Well, their parents are all rich, aren't they? They can afford to...
Yeah! AND they've all got swimming pools!
SNIFF
WE haven't!

Sophie, I'm not buying you a swimming pool...... Those friends of yours live in enormous houses with enormous gardens...
YES they DO! And they've all got videos! ..AND Sony Walkmans! AND they've got gîtes in the Périgord!

Gîtes in the Périgord! Sounds like a disease! Haaaa!
Ow, shuddup, Mum! I've got bloody NOTHING! NO WONDER they look down on me!

What did you just say, Sophie?

Your friends look down on you...because you aren't as rich as they are?
Yeah
!

SORDID attitude!
Now, Sophie ..this is serious.. now listen ....

You must know by now LIFE isn't FAIR. There are rich people and poor....
Dad and I try to bring you all up to judge people not by what they have but by what they are...

Money & having things don't mean you're a better person...
But the most repellent thing to me is when... People think they're superior just because they're more privileged...

And, my God, it's not as if YOU'RE not privileged, Sophie!
You've got a nice home...Count yourself lucky you don't live somewhere like East Street!

..and you go to a good school...
You should be thanking your lucky stars you were able to get into it....

Otherwise you'd be at that revolting school in Prosser Street...with all those nasty little thugs from the flats!
!

SORDID attitude!

Just Rewards
Today, Billy is playing host to Mummy's friend and Mummy's friend's daughter:
Billy, don't snatch the biscuits from Becky...offer them nicely!
That's right!
That's it, Billy...now no more punching, OK? Good boy!
Billy...Mummy's asking you to stop screaming....OK?
...Billy, don't say that word....
..No more throwing bricks, Billy...OK? Good boy!
God! Billy's so much more obedient, now... How've you done it?
Oh, we've got a special chart, haven't we, Bill?
Yeah!
It's Billy's special Behavior chart, isn't it?
And when Billy's a good boy and stops doing naughty things at ONCE...what does Mummy do, eh?
Gives me a star!
Right! She gives you a star to stick on your chart!
And when Billy's got so many stars on his chart...what then?
I trade them in!!
..and then we buy him something...a toy....
Well, it really seems to work!
Yes...it does...I feel I positively reinforce his good behavior...
..and, goal-wise, he always has something to aim for...
Twicycle!
Yeah..my mommy gave it me for poking people's eyes and saying shit a lot!
© Posy Simmonds

Paradise Lost

Here lie *Wendy, Belinda, Beverley & Sophie Weber*, in a state of primal bliss...washed by the sea, blessed by the sun, lulled by the murmur of a foreign tongue....
BAR

Oh isn't this heaven!

Nearby, in the shade of a fig tree, sits *George Weber (Senior Lecturer in Liberal Studies)*, rather thwarted in his attempts at cultural exchange.......
...comme Lacan a dit ..er..Lacan...Lacan, vous savez? *
Lacan?..? Ah! Lord Luc ...
er..non..
* ...as Lacan said...you know Lacan?

Ah well...
SIGH

Pommes! *
Whahaha!
BAR
* Apples

Citrons? *
?
* lemons

Ah...Poires! *
!
WHAHAA!
* Pears

Ooh..voilà une chèvre! *
Tsk!
WHAHA
* Here's a nanny-goat.

Her Hurher courgettes Ha haha
Ooh...celle-là... * ..pas mal, hein?
Hey.. Dad?
* That one..not bad, eh?

Elle est bien roulée...
..Dad! Canivergo wind-surfing? Dad! Dad!
!

EXCUSEZ-MOI, mais vous parlez de ma fille!! *
Oh..Félicitations!
* Excuse me..you're talking about my daughter!

Veuillez PAS dire ces choses tellement SEXISTES!!!

I mean, God! Honestly! D'you HAVE to force women back into stereotypes!? ...So that even PARTS of them are OBJECTS?!!
Excuse me?

I mean..your attitude.... ..NICE reflection on the commercialisation of the body!!

Going topless...can't you understand-they're not just giving you another chain to bind them with!

I mean...what would Rousseau have thought of you?...and Levy Bruhl has...
Levy-Bruhl?

YAWN
Well..all I'm saying, is: ...it's a problem that faces all us men today... ..each of us must revise our attitudes...and change our way of thinking about women.. ......

Remember when it was *Thomases'* ?

And then it became *The Purple Harvest Health Shop*.....remember?

And then that *Mrs Foxe-Forester* bought it..... turned it into *"Pot, Pine & Pinny."*......

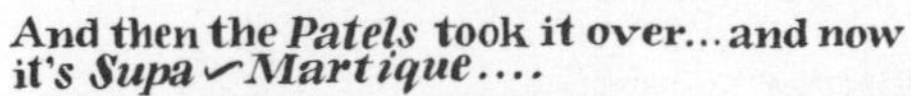
And then the *Patels* took it over... and now it's *Supa-Martique*....

Funeral Rights

One of George Weber's colleagues at the Poly has been killed in a car accident.

Today, George and Wendy attend her funeral in the country...

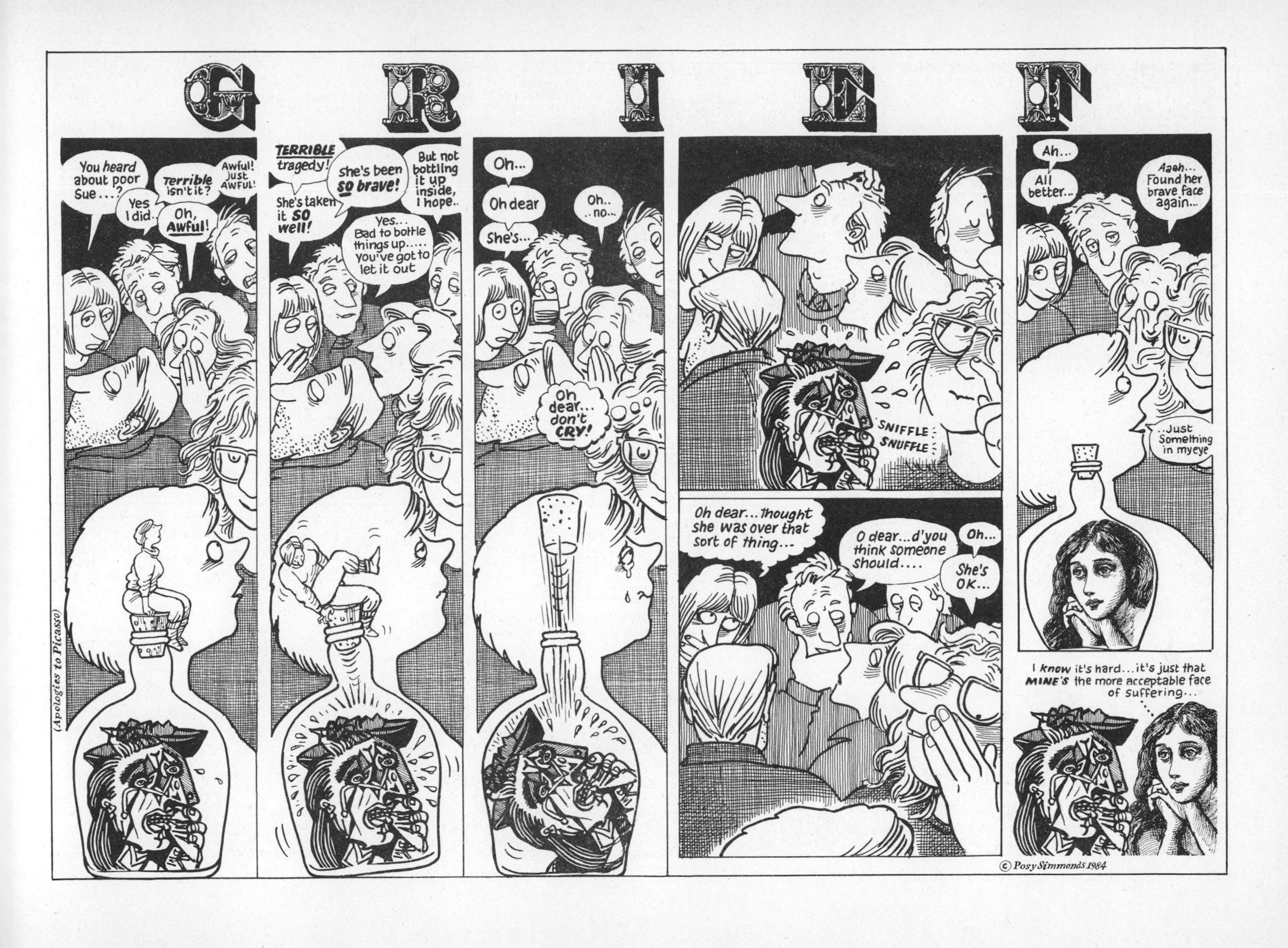
GRIEF
You heard about poor Sue...?
Yes I did..
Terrible isn't it?
Oh, Awful!
Awful! just AWFUL!
TERRIBLE tragedy!
She's taken it SO well!
She's been SO brave!
But not bottling it up inside, I hope..
Yes... Bad to bottle things up..... you've got to let it out
Oh...
Oh dear
She's...
Oh.. ..no...
Oh dear... don't CRY!
SNIFFLE SNUFFLE
Oh dear... thought she was over that sort of thing...
O dear...d'you think someone should....
Oh...
She's OK...
Ah...
All better...
Aaah... Found her brave face again...
..Just Something in myeye
I know it's hard... it's just that MINE'S the more acceptable face of suffering...
(Apologies to Picasso)
© Posy Simmonds 1984

Early September: In the mellow sunshine, *George & Wendy Weber* and their very oldest friends, turn up their toes....

TIME has faded the blossoms on the sunbeds... has eased the the tension from their rusty springs.... it has relaxed the elastic of ancient beachwear...

All is peace and innocent repose... the rustle of *Sunday Supplements* and old leaves, and the gentle rise and fall of comfy waist bands.....

Then, *Belinda Weber* & some of her friends enter the garden. ....And take a look:

And then all is not lovely in the garden....

...They are afraid because they are naked, and they hide themselves and cover their nakedness....

...all their *mottles & wattles* and *folds & flab* and *bunkles & bunions*....

THE DARK

Don't like the DARK, Manda!
Sssh Benji!

But I don't LIKE it! ....stinky!
Ssh!

Fink of howwid fings in the dark!
Aren't any horrid things!

Monsters!
Aren't any monsters

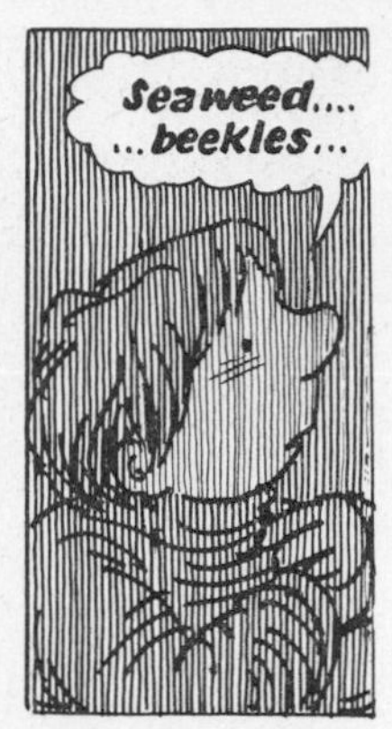
Seaweed.... ...beekles...

Aren't any beetles!
What is dere, den.. in de dark?

God..
God's in the dark...
In here?

Any-way.. I'm not afraid!
Any-way... I not afwaid!
Hee Hee Hee Hee!
Hee Hee!
Toppit!
Heee Heeee!

Ssh! Benji!
Someone coming! Someone opening the door!

BOO!
You didn't know we was in here, Mummy!
We was hidin' fwom Tamsin!

EEeAAH!

GOD! Oh GOD! Eaah! GET OUT! OUT! Out of here!!

OhmyGod! OhmyGod!!
Where's God?

They shut themselves in the old fridge...yes, the old fridge, George! They could have... AAAGH!

I know you'd dismembered the lock, George! I know! But they'd still shut the door.. tight shut! Aaagh! Aaagh!! God..

When're the Council coming? When? Tuesday! I want it picked up NOW, George! NOW!

Mummy's afwaid of the dark..

Unworthy Thoughts

Twice a month, these days, the children stay Saturday night & Sunday with their father....
Mummee! We're back!

And did you have a lovely time?
Yeah.
THINKS: I'll bet! He never makes ANY effort with them...never takes them anywhere!

Lots of video games and pin-ball?
Left them down the Amusement Arcade.. ..or in the pub garden, as usual.....

No, we didn't
What, no Space Invaders?!
God! He's lazy! Didn't take them out AT ALL!!

No! Daddy took us on a MARCH... wiv fousands of people!
Oh! The MARCH! Damn!! Clean forgot about it..... Damn! I wanted to go!

It's to stop people dropping bombs every-where....

..and to stop WARS...
..so we can grow up...
..and not have rayjo active babies...
Good to know he's con-cerned about something again..I just don't believe it.....

Did Dad know lots of people on the march?
No..
Oh....

...only Suzy...
Suzy? That a friend of his?
Tsk! What's he picked up, now..?

Yes, we went with her..She's very NICE ..she's a nurse...
Oh...

We had lovely hamburgers, Mum
'Thought you didn't like them
Tsk! Off a stand as usual! Why does he have to feed them JUNK!?

No! Daddy MADE these ones! And baked potatoes!
Oh...

He said he couldn't take us out to eat 'cos he didn't have enough money...
Didn't have enough money... my FOOT! Mean sod!

...'cos he bought us new shoes.... AND E.T. lunch boxes!
Lemmee show you!
Oooorh!!

And Suzy read us lots 'n' lots of bedtime stawies!
How lovely
SALT
So Suzy came back, did she? But, no, she didn't stay the night... did she? Not in front of the children..nooo! Because I'd get to hear of it, wouldn't I?

And did Suzy read Daddy a story?
No! She had to go on NIGHT DUTY
Oh yes, she would, wouldn't she?

Can we watch telly?
Yes, darling.
Right! Well, that does it... Hasn't put a foot wrong all weekend, has he?..new shoes ...homemade hamburgers.... sensitive girl friends!!......

Michael! What're you doing? Why're you trying to get on the right side of me!? What are you up to?!! Why're you SUCKING UP!!?

Home-Sick

CRAZY-BURGAS
BURGERS·FRIES·MILK
But darling, why did you eat all that if you felt SICK?
Why didn't you SAY?
WAIL!
I don't feel sick, Daddy! Dad! I don't ... I don't.. Dad..!

Think you're going to be sick here?
RESTAURANT
Naoooo
WAIL

Well, much better to be sick HERE... if you want to No one MINDS...... then you'll feel better
NOT here-yah! With all PEOPLE!

Well.. let's get the bus, then...
Ow, Dad! Why can't we stay out late?
Why do we have to get a BUS!?
Cos Mummy's got the car... I haven't!
Feel SICK!
Next time we'll stay out late...

Try and BE sick, then, eh?
Oooouh I feel very Sick!
uuur...

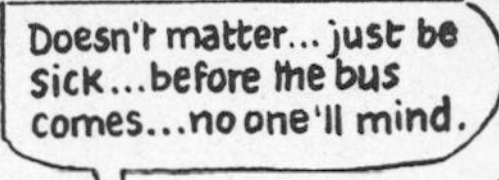
Doesn't matter... just be sick... before the bus comes... no one'll mind.

...fink I can hold on till I get HOME...
Oh GOD! Don't do that! Don't hold on till then! Please, Tara.. do it now... get it over with...
Charming!
!

Feel Si-ck!
If you're going to, do it now...

Please, Tara... don't wait till you get home.. please be sick now.... eh?

Darling.. please be sick out here.. please!
?
No!

Mummee! Gointobe Sick!
Oh God!

Oh GOD!!! All over the telephone! Look at the phone books!!

Typical! Bloody typical, Martin! Only ONE Saturday a month you have to see the kids...& what d'you do!? ...fill 'em up with bloody junk!!
We had milk shakes!

What sort of father are you...? I mean, for God's sake! Bringing her back in that state

I'm better now, Daddy!

Dad's Girl Friend
Mu-um..? You know Lynn....?
Ye-es?
HOME & MARRIAGE-BREAKER!!
She smells of all PERFUME!
DOES she? ....ooh...
YES, SHE REEKS OF IT!!
Yes! And when she tries to kiss you, it's YEURRR! HORR-UBBLE!!
IS it? Oh dear!
Stinky Poo!
...STINKS LIKE A TART'S BOUDOIR!
And she's got a.... BIG... hee hee... BOTTOM!! Hee hee hee heee!!
NOW, NOW, NOW!
HUGE BUM!
Big Boddum!
Hee Hee Hee!
When she plays BEARS with us, she looks all silly...
DOES she?
'es!
VERY SILLY!
And she doesn't do nice COOKING! Not like YOU!
She make me eat cawwots!
REALLY?
Yes! And I dowanter go to her & Daddy's at Christmas!
WHAT!?
No!
I dohwantergo there... She and Daddy whisper all the TIME!
And it's cold!
And we have to sleep on camp beds!
No No! 'course you're going ...it's all fixed!
I wantergo skiing with YOU! ...and Robert...
No, darling... you'll have a lovely, lovely time with Daddy & Lynn...
ROBERT...
You always do!
Think of Lynn's video!
Yes! She got a vidjo!
You're not to be nasty about Lynn... See?
She's very kind to you...
And she's very, very nice...
THE GUARDIAN

The cat sat on the mat.

Back to the flat, come Pat and Jack.

Jack *hates* the cat.

The cat *hates* Jack.

Pat loves the cat.

The cat loves Pat.

Pat sat on Jack's lap.

Jack pets Pat.

Jack and Pat want a nap.

Scram, cat, scram!

Drat the cat!

Oh well, the film was really ACE!

...See, this professor dude, Gabilsky, or some-ink...he's MAD an' it's googol plex years in the future an' he's planned the destruction of the world...an' he escapes in this sort of time-dilation-effect machine...an' it's really SICK cos' everything putrifies, wasn't it, Jolly? All them yellow maggots Eeuuch! An' this dude escapes but there're these other dudes in a space ship, chasing him. An' this dude is bizzing 'imself, not the professor dude, but another dude an' they run into this great particle storm, wiv all muons an' hadrons buzzin' about an' he blacks out with too many g's...not the other dude, but the professor dude...an' then he sees this other dude...

Yes, well p'raps we'll hear the rest tomorrow, chaps..

Yes, that's quite enough...off to bed now.....

DEREK'S DEADLY SINS
January: Gluttony
Feet in the trough, then, Derek!
2 pies, mash, chips and beans, right?
If you'd be so kind, Muriel!
Ooh! This looks good enough to eat!
February: Lust
I feel we almost know each other...
Stand by your bed-pans, lads... old Derek's going for a try!
Oh.. she's that bird from the building opposite our office!
April: Pride
New glasses, new clothes... Diets! What she doing to Derek, this bird?
...yes.. & what with giving up starch & sugar... I'm the same weight now as when I was eighteen!
May: Envy
Dirty old Derek... all the luck!
Looks like she'd go like a belt-fed mortar, that one!
Her her her!
How his wife doesn't find out, I just don't know!
Old enough to be her father....
July: Avarice
SOTTO VOCE: Yeah, she earns far more than we do... information technology officer.... And her Dad's got a tidy pile too..
Ah.. that's where he got his new leather jacket from!
October: Wrath
Found you out, did she, your wife? Slung you out? Ooh, dear... right old sods' opera! Poor old Derek!
Never seen her so angry...
November: Sloth
...And you look at 'em... birds... and you think why not? But after a bit, you think: I really can't be BOTHERED! I can take 'em or leave 'em, quite frankly....
VERY wise, Derek old son!
December: Gluttony
Oh, we were worried about you, Derek.. all in love... dressed up like a pox doctor's clerk...
Now, feet in the trough, Derek.. you need to put on some pork!

The Nightmare of Pauline Woodcock
Tomorrow, Pauline Woodcock (42), roving international finance correspondant for Global Investor Magazine, flies to an assignment in the Middle East....
MRS P.W. WOODCOCK BRITISH PASSPORT
...but now she sleeps....
ZZZZ
My God, I'm late! Late for the CONFERENCE!
PUFF! PUFF!
CONFERENCE
HALT! Enter not!
CONFERENCE
But I have a PASS! I've been sent to cover this conference for Global Investor Magazine!
It is FORBIDDEN for you to enter ...only MEN may!
Go there! It is ORDERED!
But... it's nothing but a Plasti-ware Party!
Look, I'm not wasting my time talking about plastic boxes with a lot of WOMEN!
Don't you realise who I AM?! I'm FINANCIAL JOURNALIST of the YEAR! I covered the IMF meeting for Panorama... I was profiled in Euromoney Magazine!
Why you no buy Plasti-ware?
Why you no husband?
Why he divorce you?
Why you no sons to cook for?
Why you no family?
Why you not able to form relationships?
Why you sit alone in room & write stories about coins all your life?
Why you avoid women's issues?
Why you despise women?
Why you closet sexist?

Diane (36, *a TV producer*) is hugging a little secret to herself.... but not for long!

Deep in the country, the cuckoo calls: *C* natural, *G sharp*...

...and in their *second home*, the Wrights (*& their guests*), nestle briefly, over the Bank Holiday.

Here, sunbeams *irradiate* & turn to *gold* a tranquil moment: Brunch *en plein air*.

All this, Jocasta captures...

...her *father's* look of calm repose, as he deliberates the *right moment* to nip down to the phone box near the pub and ring his girl friend....

...her stepmother's ruminative guise, as she wonders *how* she can *possibly* be six days overdue....

...her grandmother's *serenity* as she reflects on an awful night in a damp bed...

...her tiny half-brother's air of anticipation...

....the relaxed manner of her parents' guests ...as Paul curses his host's *stinginess* with the booze and wonders if the pub'll cash him a cheque...

...& Laura frets that the *whole* house must have heard *everything* last night, as it was only when Stanhope coughed next door, that she & Paul realised the walls were only the *flimsiest* partitions...

ALL these precious, golden moments, Jocasta captures:

HOME

'Mid pleasures and palaces, ...though we may roam......

Be it ever so humble......... there's no place like Home......

Home......Home.....

You smile a lot at people, Wendy, don't you?

Mm..suppose I do...

...and at the Pakistani lady because she's only just moved to this road... and people are a bit po-faced.......

...the socially handicapped...people you feel sorry for, who get smiles..eh?

Really Wendy!

ABC
(as it is spoken)

BRASS MONK

L.O!
2 G.n.T...
A?

I.Z., 2 G.n.T....
N.O.

Y?
I.C.U.2, B.4...
R.U. 18?

O.L!
R. 18!
O...U.R., R.U?

U.C!

C!
O!

Driving Licence
HEEP
612066
JB9117
JULIAN BARRY HEE
SCANTLEBERRY
O...I.C...
...1966..

U, 2?...18, R.U?
S!

A.R.18
R.A?....O.R.
...O.K...

2 G.n.T.?
S!

E.U.R!

F.U.2!

This is the sausage roll in question.... one of a batch prepared by the fair hand of the Dean's son...
(wodges of sausage, flaky pastry brushed with egg, left over-long in a hot oven.)

This is the fateful occasion: Each September at the Polytechnic, the Dean interrupts the remains of the vacation, *in* order that he and *Mrs* Rutland, may bid a premature *"Salvete!"* to the members of his faculty, over sherry and titbits, following a brief staff meeting...

But *George Weber* has *NO* time for cheese puffs. He is *very* concerned that the *cut-backs* in part-timers will *ruin* his new course on the culture of *Turn-of-the-Century-Vienna*......

And then the sausage roll strikes..

GLAAH

The Dean is rendered speechless.....a wodge of sausage-meat blocks his windpipe...

In just four minutes, the Dean could *expire!* How fortunate it is that George's *wife,* (an ex-nurse), is acquainted with the *Dr Henry Heimlich Manoeuvre for Chokers:*

Grasping the Dean from behind, she *thrusts* her fist upwards into his abdomen:

The offending gristle is expelled....

...and within minutes, the Dean is himself again:

This is the current bivouac catalogue:

It is filled with *100's* of exciting ideas in contemporary *home-styling*.

This is the *couldn't-be-easier* mail order form:

These are the six bivouac *stores*...... where shopping is a *pleasure-thing*....

.....where bivouac customers are free to *wander and ponder*...

...to muse 'n' choose... ...to pay 'n' take away ......

These are some typical customers, beaming from their bivouac experience, leaving the store with that special *can't-wait-to-get-it-home-&-use-it* feeling!

Here they are outside the store with that special *can't-wait-to-get-it-home-&-use-it* feeling wearing off....

And here are the bivouac *customers with that can't-wait-to-get-home-&-have-a-really-good-row* feeling....

And here are two exciting bivouac *designs in their final resting place*....

Festive Whirl
It's just one party after another, Christmas...
Mum says you've got 10 minutes to get ready...
Tsk
SIGH
I'm just NOT in the mood
I won't know anyone
Yes, you will
Dunno what to WEAR
Is it smart or what?
Can't I ring up and say I've got diarrhoea....
I'm NOT going on my OWN!!
I'll DRIVE!
You can drink all you like
Don't want to drink...
How long d'you think we need stay?
George! How lovely to see you!
let me get you a...
Well, we thought Gloucestershire for the 25th... and then back here for the New Year...
No... Jacob takes his 'A' levels next year
My God! Rufus & Jane! How long's that been going on?
Oh George! How killing!
Did you read Muspratt in the T·L·S... his Kupka/Kandinsky piece?
Oh, you mean "The Primacy of being First"?
I liked it.
Oh George! You didn't!
Terrific party!
Bye!
Lovely party Liz!
Bye Wendy!
Oh God, I did an awful thing, Wendy! I couldn't remember David Barker's wife's name!
Groan
She must have thought I was deliberately ignoring her! I feel so AWFUL!
Oh, don't WORRY!
Honestly, George... everyone was so plastered, they won't remember.
Why did I encourage him to gossip about Mark, in front of.....
SIGH
Wish I'd talked more to Ken
...should have spoken to old Taylor...
Wish I hadn't said that...
SIGH
Oo...why did I?...
Dunno what Harriet thinks now..
...should have...
...but why does drink make me so horribly PRIGGISH...?
Just wish I hadn't said...
...won't get asked again...
P'raps I'll ring Liz up and thank her for last night...
I like parties!
Muesli
Another festivity tonight?
Yes, the Thomases.

It's *quite* a worry, one's country cottage, this polar weather...one *has* to drive out there and check the pipes haven't done anything *ghastly*.....

But *Help* is soon summoned:

And Help is soon diligently going about its business....

Diligently...diligently he works.....

Long job...take day or two with hair-dryers, melting THAT! Draughty old place, like this...

...until, beneath him, he hears the lady's voice, telephoning her husband....

eh?

!

Salt of the Earth! I'll give urr Salt of the Earth, I will!

No! You wouldn't get that sort of service in *town*! You'd just get some frightful COWBOY.... yes! All spaghetti pipe-work!

Just going to make him a nice cuppa...got no milk ...hope he doesn't mind POWDERED.... What? Sugar? Oh yes, I'll put lots of sugar in.. they always take sugar, don't they! Yes...he's such a NICE little man..

And the angry plumber turns from the greater toil..... and commits an act of lightning pipe-work in the downstairs loo....

Marriage à la Mode

What!? Belinda wants to get **married!?** **NO!?** My God, **WHO** to?

To... this *Alistair*... one of the **directors** she helps cook for... **well, I** don't call it **COOKING**... What they **EAT** in that directors' dining room! You wouldn't **BELIEVE!**
FLOUR

...**Whipped cream**... lime jelly... .... **crushed** ginger biscuits ..... it's **SUPPOSED** to be **Cordon Bleu**....
salt
But it's more **Cordon Bleu-ch-ch!**

But, this is very sudden...
No... they've been carrying on some time....
So it seems

But, what's he **like**, this..?
Oh... **28**-ish... enormous income.. ..drives a **SAAB**..
SIGH
Oh **dear**!

They plan to live in his **mews** flat to start with.....

But Belinda can still work at her **career**, Wendy....
CAREER!
Huh!
That's the *last* thing she says she wants!

What's she going to do with **herself**, then, for Godsake? She's not **pregnant**, is she?
No, if she was, we'd be more understanding

Oh, she'll keep herself very **BUSY**... going to the **hairdresser**... arranging **daffodils**..... making **crême brûlée**...

All those **A levels** she's got.... The **WASTE!!**
It's ***so irresponsible!*** What's she going to do when the marriage **folds**? How's she going to support herself **then**?
She doesn't **THINK!**

Well, it's her **bed**.. she's got to lie on it...
Bloody comfy BED... she's ordering it at **Harrods**!

And she wants a ***huge, WHITE*** wedding....
NO!
Yes... and she wants poor George to **GIVE** her away-***can you imagine?***- like a chattel
NO!

How could Belinda ***do*** this to you!?...... ...After **ALL** you've...
I know!
We had such hopes for her...
SIGH
Where did we go wrong...?
I dunno ***what*** the neighbours'll say.....
Still, what can you do?... we'll stand by her... she ***is*** our daughter, after all...
I think I lay the blame at the feet of ***Princess Diana*** ..she set the young a terrible example

World of Work
PEARL

Noo...nothing much doing in the beavering dept. this afternoon...so I thought...b*gg*r this for a box of soldiers...I'm OFF!
Same here....I've sloped off...done some Christmas Shopping....

Ooh...that's a chintzy little diary.....
Yeah...got it for Dad.. ..only simulated...REAL gilt edges...had it personalised for him
Vurry acceptable!
Diary 1985

Any more fares?
Let's see...How many days do we get off, next Christmas?

Ooh!..stand by your bed-pans! 25th's a Wednesday! so that's ...1...2...3...4 ...5...6...7, 8...
Well...should clear 14 days ...no sweat...

Last year, I only wangled eleven days off....
Yes... Could Do Better, old son.
Diary 1985

PEARL
What about this year?

Well...I skive off early Thursday ...get Friday, 21st off, Christmas shopping....then it's 1...2...3... 4...5 days off over the holiday ....

Yees..then it's nearly the weekend.... and then you get 1,2,3,4,5 days, New Year....forget Wednesday the 2nd.... and the 3rd...no one goes in, do they? It's like a TOMB....

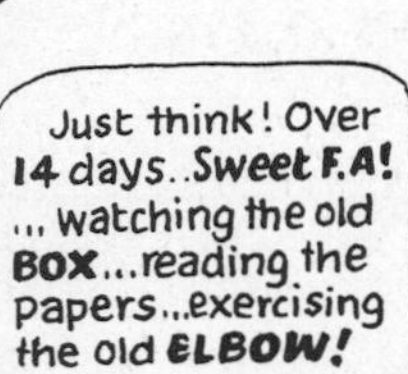
Just think! Over 14 days..Sweet F.A! ... watching the old BOX...reading the papers...exercising the old ELBOW!

Oh no... don't think I'm skiving off the 28th..... ...said I'd go in....
EH?
Yeah, well I might feel a bit GUILTY....

You GREAT toilet! Who in their right minds wants to WORK?

WAH!

!
GORDON BENNETT! ...why he do that!?

Oh...

JOB CENTRE
!

SHAME

Yes...it's only a *card*, wishing the family all the Joy of *An Olde-Fashioned Xmas*.. ...and a handsome fruit cake, baked according to *Mrs Trivet's* ancient recipe, for the *Edwardian Nobility*.....

Well... NO stagecoaches, for a start....

Oh

And all that remains in the wintry waste, is Peace and Goodwill ....and the Chill Breath of the Future *gusts* across the plain ... and, on it, the sound of *Something Hungry*, howling beyond the horizon ..... *shivering* the very cones of the sentinel pines.....

Frightfully late, one Christmas Eve....

Darling, it's two poor **hippie types**... only they've got nowhere to stay tonight... the **PUB'S** got no room.....

...and **she's** frightfully **PREG**... looks as if she's going to **POP** any minute!

Oh God... well... we'd better sort them out...

All of us are joining in,
And wishing all our friends...
Christmas!
Greetings
Christmas Greetings!
To all the family
Merry Christmas and a Happy New Year
RIOJA
A peaceful Yule and bright New Year,
No matter what portends.
Christmas!
Greetings
Christmas Greetings!
M.O.D. KEEP OUT
RIOJA

A MESSAGE TO

The MONSTROUS Regiment

FROM: Field Marshal Sir Desmond Blundel-Bolass, and the Massed Captains of Industry, and Chiefs of the Market Forces.

(Regimental Insignia of the Monstrous)

...otherwise, COMPLETE SHAMBLES!

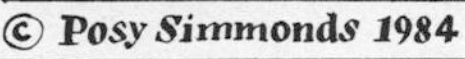

Poo!